CW00537840

Caring for Carol by Ca

CARING
for CAROL
by Caring for Me

A Journey with Dementia and Self–Discovery

ANTHONY P. MAURO SR.

Foreword by Renowned Neurologist Gayatri Devi, MD

LUMINARE PRESS
WWW.LUMINAREPRESS.COM

Printed in the United States of America

Luminare Press
442 Charnelton St.
Eugene, OR 97401
www.luminarepress.com

LCCN: 2024900667
ISBN: 979-8-88679-471-7

To Carol, it's a privilege to share my life,
love, and journey with you.

To Anthony Jr. and Tori, be assured
that you're in the dedications of the other books
I've authored but neither of you have opened.
Seriously, Mom and I love you both dearly.

To Dr. Devi, the compassion with which you treat your
patients is perhaps more effective than any medicine.
Thank you.

To those who find wonder in the ordinary.

TABLE *of* CONTENTS

Foreword
by Dr. Gayatri Devi

This is the story of Carol and Anthony, two people who fell in love in their twenties, married, and raised a family. At fifty-nine, as prospects of retirement and grandparenthood beckoned from a rosy future, Carol was diagnosed with frontotemporal degeneration (FTD), a form of dementia. The symptoms had been creeping up over the previous two years, initially misdiagnosed as depression. How would Anthony and Carol cope?

It helped that Carol and Anthony were both we-will-do-anything-for-those-we-love, glass-half-full folk. Throughout this deeply personal and moving book, you will encounter the overarching theme of celebrating what is left rather than mourning what was lost. This is not to say that Anthony and Carol did not struggle with this many-tentacled being called dementia as they travelled down life's road together.

After Carol's diagnosis, Anthony was overwhelmed with tremendous compassion for what she must have gone through before her diagnosis. Formerly meticulous, she began making mistakes in her administrative job, prompting retirement. Anthony writes, "She must have been feeling lost and overwhelmed at work. I felt terrible for not knowing it."

As Carol became less independent, Anthony juggled planning for the future with living in the moment. His struggle is all our struggles. Who among us does not aim to be more in the present? Anthony proves to be an excellent teacher. He embraces life "as it is when it cannot be changed to what I want it to be." I am reminded of what my grandfather used to say: "What cannot be cured has to be endured." Anthony wanted to not merely endure but to find joy and meaning in his role, in his situation. How could he?

Unbeknownst to him, Anthony had, for much of his life, been preparing for the role of caregiver. As a young boy and teenager, he suffered from anxiety and panic attacks. Embarrassed by his illness, he kept it secret. He managed his crippling symptoms through a combination of behavioral and desensitization techniques. Each day, he devised multiple means to meet goals, small and large. Through these methods and with professional help, he achieved success in his personal and professional life.

Anthony now finds joy in daily victories. He writes that it is his "mission…to make Carol laugh." He is delighted when Carol, a talented archer, scores a bull's-eye when the family goes on vacation. The blessing of Carol's type of dementia is that she has lost insight into her deficiencies and instead is living very much in the moment. When the usually decorous Carol, disinhibited by her dementia, loudly calls him the handsomest man in a crowded room, Anthony chooses to revel in the compliment rather than cringe. As her dementia progresses, Carol laughs and giggles throughout the day. Anthony is glad that she has found a way to live in "unremitting happiness." She claps her hands when she is happy, and in her incessant clapping, he hears her joy rather than the nuisance some others did.

Anthony P. Mauro Sr.

Even as he revels in these daily triumphs, Anthony acknowledges that Carol is losing her "charm, her ability to problem solve, our shared memories…our intimacy." He notes the "loss of stability in our lives…the loss of hope… the loss of a sense of security."

At my office, Carol wrote her granddaughter's name when asked to but perseverated, writing "Charli" again when asked to write her husband's name, unable to mentally "switch tracks." Her apraxia (inability to perform previously learned tasks) meant she needed more help with daily activities such as toileting. Carol began to have trouble with the mechanics of walking, sitting, chewing, and even swallowing food. While Anthony continued to support her when needed, the constant demand was wearing him down.

Anthony made a conscious decision to keep and care for Carol at home. Carol's mother, who also had dementia, had spent her last years in a nursing home, but Anthony chose a more difficult path. In the latter half of the book, Anthony gives important advice about home-based medical care, why a "physician order of life-sustaining treatment" is useful, and other practical advice for caregivers. He weighs the pros and cons of having an aide as a part of one's intimate family circle.

At one juncture, caregiver guilt assails Anthony as he enjoys the fun of his first solo car ride in several years. Carol is at home with her aide. He looks over sadly at the "empty passenger seat" but knows he needs a little time for himself.

Lucky for us, Anthony, at the behest of a therapist he saw briefly, decided to write a book about his experience. He reveals that he found the key to acceptance in Zen Buddhism, which anticipates and embraces sorrow, illness, death, and change as events we will all experience and as the natural order of life.

Anthony finds caregiving "a positive experience" and not "a burden as some might think." He writes that "we are made whole by selfless service to the needs of others." While caregiving is a Sisyphean task of "rolling a boulder up a mountain and watching it roll back down," Anthony finds the daily tasks of caregiving to be meditative. Camus' essay on Sisyphus concludes, "The struggle itself towards the heights is enough to fill a man's heart. One must imagine Sisyphus happy."

Our Sisyphus, Anthony, has found happiness in his repetitive, daily chores. He concludes by affirming that in caring for Carol, he has found the best way to care for himself. The two are one and the same.

People often ask me if my job is depressing. They ask because I am a physician who helps men and women with dementia, both patients and caregivers, navigate their illness. With the privilege of knowing people like Carol and Anthony, how can I be anything but inspired and renewed every day? I am the luckiest physician in the world! Thank you, Carol, and thank you, Anthony!

— Gayatri Devi, MD, MS, FAAN

Author's note: Dr. Devi is a peer-chosen Super Doctor in the top 5 percent of New York City neurologists. Her approach to Alzheimer's disease was published in *The New England Journal of Medicine*. She is a widely published author and has been interviewed on media outlets including CBS, NPR, *60 Minutes*, *The New York Times*, and *The Wall Street Journal*.

Preface

My wife, Carol, was fifty-nine years old when she was diagnosed with frontotemporal degeneration (FTD), a form of dementia, and it was completely unexpected. In addition to the challenge of providing firsthand care for her and coping with the physical and emotional aspects of her illness, I have spent a lifetime dealing with anxiety, depression, panic disorder, and agoraphobia.

FTD is caused by a group of disorders that gradually damage the frontal and temporal lobes. These damages cause changes in thinking and behavior. Symptoms can include unusual behaviors, emotional problems, trouble communicating, challenges with work, and difficulty with walking. FTD is progressive, meaning symptoms get worse over time. It is a rare type of dementia and tends to occur at a younger age than other dementias. Most people with FTD are forty-five to sixty-four years old, and the disease can be hard to diagnose, because the symptoms are like other conditions. Because it is uncommon, physicians may be unfamiliar with the signs and symptoms.

Some people live more than ten years after diagnosis while others live less than two. There is no cure for FTD and no way to slow down or prevent it. However, there are ways to help manage the symptoms.

After three years of caring for Carol while running my home-based business, a friend who had found herself in a similar situation recommended I talk with a therapist, and I gave it a try. After three sessions, the therapist and I agreed that it wasn't something I needed to continue, but based on our conversations, she suggested I write a book, because my approach to life and the way I manage adversity would be helpful to others.

It never occurred to me that the way I live would have value to anyone. I often keep to myself and enjoy my own space, and when I do connect with people, it is usually on a deeper level. I didn't know what I would say in a book, how I would say it, or whether anyone would find what I had to say helpful.

Several months later, I had a Forrest Gump moment. I started running and kept running, or in my case, I started writing and kept writing. After a while, I had written enough, and the writing stopped. Why did I do it? To exploit Mr. Gump's answer, I just felt like writing. As the therapist had suggested, the result might be of service to others.

Between the covers of this book is a timeline for readers to learn about FTD and observe its progression. Families, friends, caregivers, and those who need to hire caregivers will get a glimpse at what they can expect physically and emotionally when confronting FTD or other forms of dementia.

For those who like to psychoanalyze, there are plenty of opportunities to peer into the workings of my mind. I've detailed a calming method that I use to manage panic attacks born of anxiety, depression, panic disorder, and agoraphobia, and it has helped me lead a full, productive life. Carol's diagnosis became a conduit that awakened me to life and the immediacy of each moment.

The spiritual among us will find a method of meditation I've used for the past three years to help dissolve anxiety and realize equanimity. Practicing the meditation method can help us use suffering to increase awareness of ourselves and transform pain into joy. It helps me to care for myself and improves my ability to care for Carol. The result enriches the quality of our lives.

Finally, for those who believe compassion is the heart of humanness, this book is my testimony.

Be thankful for a blessing; a blessing is a gift that adds quality to one's life. Be indebted to adversity; overcoming adversity is a gift that adds quality to oneself.

Anthony P. Mauro Sr.

JULY 2018

After the Beginning

My wife, Carol, and I boarded a train headed for New York City, and I knew the area well. The station was in the town where we bought our first home, Aberdeen, New Jersey. It was a tiny, one-bedroom condominium furnished with all the love that could fit inside.

The unit was nestled behind trees that were buffers to a busy street and had a swath of grass on two sides that offered a feeling of privacy, though privacy was relative when living in a condo complex. We weren't the first owners, but it was newly made with a beige brick exterior that gave it an up-to-the-minute look, at least to my eyes.

As our relationship grew, so did the other aspects of our lives: children, ambitions, and all the responsibilities that come with adulthood. These concerns motivated us to move into a modest, three-bedroom home two years later.

Life seemed much simpler back then. No, I'll correct myself—it *was* simpler—but Carol and I experienced such an ample life for more than three decades that to consider trading our lives now for our lives then would be like trading champagne for beer.

My thoughts were a welcome distraction from our mission, like reading a magazine while sitting in the waiting room of a dentist's office—a form of repression, a way to divert the mind from anxiety that rooted in the pit of the stomach while waiting your turn to have the sharp end of a needle pierce a receding gumline and a throttled drill carve out a cavity on a molar that should have received attention years earlier.

We were traveling to meet with a neurologist about Carol's symptoms. I had taken her to more than a few doctors, trying to understand her growing behavioral changes: a general practitioner, a psychiatrist, a neurologist, a second psychiatrist, and a second neurologist. After one and a half years of entering and exiting waiting rooms without a diagnosis, I didn't have any confidence today would be different, but we are on our way to finding out the results of a test of Carol's spinal fluid sample.

The subtle behavioral changes had made me question whether something was wrong. A few years earlier, we celebrated Christmas Eve at Carol's brother's house with her immediate relatives. We had a wonderful time, as we did every year. I was talking my way through the crowd and would occasionally swing around to be with her, then move on to the next assemblage like a socialite. I didn't pay much attention to what she was eating or drinking, as I knew her routines fluently and didn't expect any changes to them.

When we arrived home, she excused herself and went up to the bathroom to vomit. She had drunk too much wine. It was out of character for Carol, a person with a habit, if not a rule, of stopping at one glass. Our adult kids and I had a good laugh at her expense, and she took it in good nature.

A few days later, we were on vacation in Naples, Florida. We hadn't been away in years, and now that we were

Anthony P. Mauro Sr.

approaching empty nest status, we considered pulling up stakes to move to the southern city. Such a move would be a tremendous change, since we had lived our entire lives in the metro New York City area of New Jersey.

The landscape and weather in Florida were vastly different, and the people had a slower pace when they talked, walked, and drove. It wouldn't have surprised me if it applied to how they breathed. To add to the differences, Naples was a thousand miles away from our kids, parents, brothers, and sisters.

These considerations weighed heavily on my mind at the end of our stay. While driving the rental car back to the airport, I asked Carol what she thought about relocating to Florida. I was more than surprised when she said, "I can do it." It didn't seem as if she had considered any of the concerns I had, which was out of character. When I mentioned this, she shrugged them off and repeated, "I can do it."

Carol's frustration with the grocery shopping had become a weekly topic. I didn't know why since she'd been doing it since the day we were married. In the first few years of our marriage, I helped her, but as life and responsibilities became more complicated, she did the chore alone. She now complained that thinking about creating a grocery list was a problem. I thought maybe shopping tedium was getting to her. She complained for a month, and I wrote a list for her since we bought mostly the same things each week. I thought that having a prewritten list would help, but it didn't.

There were other symptoms, some downright unexplainable, but I wanted to think about something other than the mission we were on, and the monotonous clickity-clack of the train as it rocked along the rails was like easy listening music—soothing, relaxing, and perfect for my mind to be elsewhere. I looked out the window at the passing scenery. At one point, the congestion of the suburban landscape was split open, revealing a large marshland, creek, and bay. I craned my neck, looking for the ducks that settled in the waterways: usually mallards, black ducks, and occasionally mergansers.

The train unexpectedly stopped, though we weren't at the next station. I pressed my face against the window, looking for the cause, and saw the winding Matawan Creek passing in front of our location. The din in the train car went silent, and people looked up from their phones and newspapers to acknowledge each other for the first time. They let their cocked eyebrows do their talking as if to ask, "What's going on?" Someone whispered, "Ugh, the bridge is stuck open again." A collective sigh of disgust followed. All eyes returned to their forms of entertainment, and after a ten-minute delay, the train continued.

Carol's preoccupation was station stops. There were ten along the route: South Amboy, Perth Amboy, Woodbridge, Rahway, Linden, Elizabeth, Newark Airport, Newark Penn Station, Secaucus, and New York Penn Station. She was determined to announce our arrival at each one along the way and with more enthusiasm than the short, round conductor who barked them devotedly past a thick, bristled mustache. Carol was so absorbed in her ritual that she talked about the next station just as we were leaving the last. It was a compulsion that reversed on our trip back home.

Compulsions were one more symptom that initiated the medical fact-finding journey that led us New York City.

Hot City Life

The train finally came to a jolting halt at New York Penn Station. You could always tell the final stop by the anxiousness of those who hurried to position themselves as close to the doors as possible before the train rolled to a stop. They exited like sprinters from starting blocks, only there was no starter's gun, just a slit of light that squeezed through a sliding door as it opened and launched the rat race.

We exited the air-conditioned confines and were met by a blast of dank, disgusting air. The dungeon-like atmosphere of the Penn Station subterrane made the steamy air seem as if particles of filth were suspended in it. It was a foul experience, at least for me. We were swept into a herd of eager people bumping off each other like marbles shook in a jar. We jockeyed our way into the narrow opening of the escalator and pressed against bodies in a way that in any other scenario would be considered molestation. We were corralled cattle, nothing more.

I held Carol's hand so she wouldn't be swallowed by the mass of sticky-skinned bodies. Most people were dressed in business attire and carried professional-looking gear. It amused me that the reason for their mad dash was to get to a place they'd rather not be: their job. I smiled to myself as I likened it to sprinting to one's funeral, but I understood the motive too well, being a victim of the predicament myself.

We made our way past rows of cave-like terminal corridors and exited on Eighth Avenue. It was a northbound street. I was correcting a mistake I made on our first visit when I chose Seventh Avenue and had to head south in a cab before then making our way north in New York City traffic. It could be a lesson in patience even for the saints, but I suspect that they, too, would murmur obscenities to themselves.

On the sidewalk was a homeless man in the shabbiest of clothing, propped against a wall. He had an untamed beard, a few belongings, even fewer teeth, and deep lines on his face that I imagined were faint wrinkles only years before. He was lying in a pool of his own urine. I paused and watched him go unnoticed by the migrating crowd. He was a gray pixel in a black-and-white landscape. I tried to conceive the response of people if the same helpless, neglected figure had been propped on a curb in the suburban town in which they lived. I don't think even one of the commuters would fail to call 911 to assist him. We can be adaptive creatures given the environment in which we find ourselves, so adaptive as to be cruelly desensitized.

I was equally guilty. I looked away to hail a cab, surrendering to defeat in being able to change this man's circumstances. In fact, I was more guilty than the others, since I took the time to consider his plight. He didn't seem to exist to anyone else.

A cabbie saw my outstretched arm and swerved across lanes, competing with another equally reckless taxi driver. Honking horns, four-letter words, and a hastily erected middle finger commemorated the event. The heat wave and traffic jams were so oppressive that the usual city discourtesies were aggravated and amplified. As quickly as this stir was created, it was quickly enveloped by the mass of city hum, and life continued.

We sat ourselves in the cab, and I noticed the humidity trapped in the tiny confines. There was a stale odor, nothing foul but nonetheless unpleasant. I expected to find relief from the brutal heat, but the taxi's air conditioning system

Anthony P. Mauro Sr.

was unable to handle the strain put upon it by the oppressively humid weather. I knew the driver had surmised the problem, because he had made the effort to buy corrugated tubing, connect one end to the vents in the front of the vehicle, and stretch it between the front seats so that the air flowed to the rear of the car where we were seated. I would have thanked him for his ingenuity but for the fact that the design, though well intended, was thoroughly useless. I saved my breath for a potential conversation that never materialized.

The city had a flow. It moved to its own music. You became caught in the tempo, and trying to change it was hopeless, so it was best to let it carry you to your destination without resentment. We passed vertical store facades pressing against each other. It was hard to tell where one building ended and the next began, as only the names emblazoned on them gave a clue.

Carol asked in an innocent tone if I wanted to stop to shop in one of them, unaware of the time constraints we faced. Asking impulsive and unreasoned questions was another symptom. Our appointment with Dr. Gayatri Devi was at noon, and while we were on schedule, if we were to go shopping, we would be hours late.

The Doctor's Inn

We pulled up to the street address, an apartment building off Park Avenue. A large, green awning protruded to the street, and we made our way under it into a foyer. Off to the right of the apartment elevator was an unpretentious door that looked like it would open into a little utility room instead of an office. Once we were on the other side of it, we met the staff. They were so cordial and inviting that it felt as if they added spaciousness to the narrow confines of the waiting area.

Carol didn't question the reasons for visiting all the doctors she'd seen in the past year and a half or the tests she'd undergone. None had been able to diagnose her symptoms. I explained what we are doing, and she willingly went along with me. It was her nature to be unassuming and quiet and to carry herself with dignity. She was intelligent and could be playfully silly with her family. These were qualities that had endeared her to me since the beginning of our relationship.

We were standing in front of a nicely dressed, polite receptionist. She may have been a bit older than me, and she welcomed us with a warm voice while offering chocolates in gold wrapping from a plate on her desk. I loved chocolate and could tell it was excellent quality. With my mouth full of it, I found myself mumbling my way through introducing Carol to the staff. She was also preoccupied with the chocolate and reached for a second piece before completely chewing the first. I was not quick enough to stop her, and her cheeks became filled pouches. Everyone saw humor in the indignity and warmly smiled.

By now, I was used to waiting areas in doctor's offices. The older practices had sofas and chairs, white or gray walls, a lone plant stuck in a corner, and tatty magazines stuffed tightly into racks. The newer practices exchanged the staid look for one that was bright, clean, and natural with a color TV hawking pharmaceutical solutions to nearly every existing disease and a list of side effects that made me wonder if I was better off defying a prescription for them.

This office was tasteful and original. The furnishings seemed to reflect the owner's likings, not those pitched in sales brochures that were so nondescript they betrayed any natural quality. An inner office door opened, and there stood a slight figure: a woman of obvious Indian descent with perfect skin, shiny black hair, impeccably arched eyebrows, a confident posture, and dark eyes. Her persona was a mixture of medical professional and dignitary. She said amiably, "Come on in, Carol."

Dr. Devi was a nationally recognized expert in the diagnosis and management of cognitive disorders. I could create a lengthy list of her awards and credentials, so many of which were displayed that she had run out of wall space, but what was equally impressive were her personable, caring ways.

Carol and I sat in comfortable, fashionable chairs in front of Dr. Devi's desk. Her dogs, Lola and Huckleberry, were in the room. Lola was a certified therapy and service dog that had appeared on *CBS News* and was featured in an article in *The Wall Street Journal* on dogs in doctors' offices.

I noticed Dr. Devi's face strain a bit as she lifted her eyes from the papers in her hand. She spoke deliberately, and each word increasingly agitated my mind. I was overwhelmed and stupefied as I slowly processed her words. A bolt of panic shot through me, and adrenaline-laced thoughts raced with such speed that I couldn't recognize them. I felt my chest become tight. My hands tightly gripped the arms of the chair, my jaw went slack, and my eyes widened. I gradually rejoined reality and the conversation. "What do you mean, the results show there's an eighty percent chance of Creutzfeldt-Jakob disease, fifteen percent chance of frontotemporal degeneration, or five percent chance of Lewy body disease?"

She repeated the sentence she had said moments before.

Still stunned, I asked, "What is Creutzfeldt-Jakob disease?"

Dr. Devi empathetically delivered a horrible description. "It is a rapidly progressive, invariably fatal, neurodegenerative disorder." She paused, her eyes portending concern. "You should expect Carol's mind and body to deteriorate quickly." Plenty of caring words led to her repeating the diagnosis, but I don't remember any of them. I was focused on the harshest. Dr. Devi must have sensed my confusion and inability to absorb the gravity of her words. I asked what symptoms I could expect.

In a soft tone, she said, "Mr. Mauro, if it is Creutzfeldt-Jakob disease, you should be prepared for her to experience loss of coordination, changes in personality and behavior, disorientation, convulsions, muscle twitching, and…"

I didn't hear the rest of her description. My mind had shut down, and my hand stopped scribbling illegible notes on the pad I had brought with me. I became mindful that Carol was seated next to me. I turned to her, expecting to see her in a state of shock. Dr. Devi's diagnosis and prognosis were directed at her, but Carol was unfazed, as if the doctor's words were easy conversation.

I tried to repeat "Creutzfeldt-Jakob" but characteristically botched the words, so they were unrecognizable.

Carol corrected me, saying, "KROITS-felt YAH-kobe." She had a great ability to hear complicated names and remember them immediately. She looked at me and Dr. Devi and asked, "So I don't have Alzheimer's, like my mother?"

In an act of compassion and honesty, Dr. Devi assured her that Creutzfeldt-Jakob was not Alzheimer's disease.

That was all the relief she needed. At fifty-nine years of age, Carol could not grasp the harsh reality that had just hijacked our lives: an incurable neurological disease classified as dementia. We now had an answer, a heartbreaking answer, to a litany of formerly unanswered questions about her symptoms.

Dr. Devi's attention turned to Carol, allowing me to pull together my frayed thoughts and compartmentalize my overwhelming emotions. I wanted to appear settled and collected for Carol's sake. I did not want my demeanor or expression to convey urgency. If Carol was relieved with the diagnosis and happy with life, I saw no reason to make her think otherwise. *To what end?* I thought. My brain switched to autopilot. My mission was to get home where I could absorb what had happened in private. We collected our things and left.

I held Carol's hand as we walked to the corner of Park Avenue. I hailed a cab, mumbled "Penn Station" to the driver, and off we went.

A Long Ride Home

The cab seemed more confining than the one we rode in to the doctor's office, but it was the same make and model. I knew the cause of my anxiety was not vehicle design. The stop-and-go traffic made me feel each inch of road we traveled, and I wanted to jump out of both my head and the cab.

The midday heat and humidity were suffocating and choked the air conditioner to the point of being useless. The skin of my arms stuck to the vinyl upholstery. This cabbie didn't bother relying on ingenuity to create a makeshift airflow system like our earlier driver. I suspected this guy had conceded defeat to the molten air. Despite the torture, I pulled myself together and began small talk with Carol but thought, *Small talk? Am I at a point to make trivial conversation with a woman I've been married to for more than thirty years?* The idea would have been inconceivable only twenty minutes earlier.

At this point in our marriage, we were as comfortable with silence as we were with conversation. Now, I found myself entertaining Carol as nervously as if we were on a first date. After about ten minutes of forced conversation, I was calm enough to see that she was just as happy looking at traffic as she was hearing me talk. We slipped back into the flow of our normal pattern, which was the simple, silent pleasure of being in each other's company.

My silence was of voice, not thought. Overpowering anxiety now piled on my history with anxiety. Forty years earlier, I'd had a mental health crisis of depression, panic disorder, and agoraphobia. The panic attacks caused overwhelming fear, and between episodes, there was the constant dread about when and where the next one would occur. It could be brought about by life-changing events, and surely Carol's diagnosis qualified as one. I began wondering whether the stress I faced now might cause a recurrence.

The reality of being in the taxi with Carol dragged me out of my daydream. If there was one blessing at the moment, it was Carol's inability to process the gravity of our situation. It was a painfully slow ride to Penn Station, and my anxious state seemed magnified by the city noises, the car jolting on uneven streets, the fits and starts of bumper-to-bumper traffic, the race to outmaneuver other drivers, and the heat wave. I knew that once we arrived at our stop, there remained a long, laboring train ride home.

I looked out the window at the crowded sidewalks and expressions on people's faces as a distraction from my ruminations. I tried to imagine what might be happening in their lives: marriage, divorce, pregnancy, troubled children, a job promotion or loss, illness, stress, etc. Only hours before, they would have simply been part of the scenery to me—pieces, sections, and elements of a massive city board game.

We arrived at Penn Station, and I was finally rescued from the cramped, sweltering confines of the taxi. I swung open the door to a sense of freedom, though I knew it would be lost when we boarded the train. Now, I was not in a generous mood to contemplate the homeless people while walking through the station.

We stood among the masses, listening for the announcement of the train's gate, and when "Gate 12" boomed from the PA system, bodies rushed madly to the assigned entrance. We were swept into a mob and carried to the gate opening where we merged like waggling bottles onto a conveyor line. I don't care for crowds, and I try not to think like them, since the nature of a crowd is to do very little thinking.

Carol was again preoccupied with the station stops along our route home, this time in reverse: Secaucus, Newark Penn Station, Newark Airport, Elizabeth, Linden, Rahway, Woodbridge, Perth Amboy, South Amboy, and Aberdeen. She announced each one with the same enthusiasm as she had on our way to New York City.

More Symptoms

We arrived home, and I made the best of our routines. I picked up the remote, settled Carol in front of the TV, turned on her favorite program, kissed her and told her I loved her, and headed upstairs to my office.

I sat in my chair and looked at the demands of my business that had accrued during my absence; fifteen emails, a column of yellow Post-it notes running down the wall in front of my desk with written reminders, and a blinking red light on my desk phone that I resented for demanding that I hurry and listen to the messages. None of it mattered. At that moment, I was ready to walk away from my business. My anguish made it seem like I could. I was drained. I could think only about Carol, and my thoughts bounced between prized memories and her horrible diagnosis. I thought of the incidents that had led me to Dr. Devi, prompting her to do the spinal fluid test.

Carol and I had flown to Detroit more than a year earlier to celebrate our friend's sixtieth birthday. It was January, the weather was in single digits, and snow was quickly accumulating. We had left behind the same conditions in New Jersey. I assumed Carol had packed accordingly for our trip, and there was no reason to think otherwise.

We left our hotel for the party and were smacked with a blast of frigid wind. I was helping Carol into our taxi and noticed she wasn't wearing stockings. I asked her if she was cold, and she said no. I also noticed that her dress was understated for the party, which was odd for her. For as long as I'd known her, she'd been very attentive to the appropriate fashion for events. She was a meticulous dresser. She held her family to the same exacting standards of dress, and I was on the losing side of arguments, asserting that we could dress casually when attending informal holiday celebrations.

I didn't give much more thought to her fashion sense in Detroit but did ask her why she was dressed inappropriately for the weather. Her answer was a shrug.

On our flight home, she wore open-toed shoes, knowing that we would walk through snow to get to our parked car. As we exited the terminal, I watched her step in snow that covered her bare toes, but she was unfazed. I asked if her feet were cold, not believing for a moment they couldn't be, but she shook her head.

Carol wore the same sweater most days. She had thrown a good piece of Tupperware in the garbage along with the dated food it contained. Not long ago, she had begun pacing around the house, and when I asked why, she said it made her feel good. On Christmas Day when we opened presents with our family, she didn't give her gifts to me. I knew she had them in the bedroom closet but had to politely prompt her to get them.

She impulsively bought $130 worth of a natural sleep remedy, a total of five bottles, from a second-rate TV ad and never considered the price, how much she'd use, whether they were effective, or if the unopened bottles could be returned for a refund.

Hard Calls

When my office phone rang, it snatched me from thinking of the past and delivered me to the present. I ignored it. I had to call Carol's siblings, Lee and Lynn, with the result of the visit. Until that point, Carol's diagnosis was just words in my mind, but now that I was about to say the words out loud, I sensed it would bring reality and inevitability to them. My final defense mechanism, denial, was about to be shattered. I searched for the courage to speak.

I dialed Lee's number. I hadn't realized the pressure that had been building all day as I held everything inside, trying to act normally for Carol as we commuted home. I counted three rings, and Lee answered. I opened my mouth, and the day's nightmare erupted like a volcano. Lee responded in disbelief, "Whaaat!?"

That's the last thing I remember about the conversation. I became undone. I later learned that Lee had received my call in the middle of a crowded airport while waiting to board a flight home. I felt terrible about the poor timing.

The conversation was cathartic enough for me to compose myself and call Lynn. Her shock and concern at the news manifested in a litany of questions, and each of my answers doubled the questions. Lynn was looking for assurances and options, but I could give her neither. The cruel reality was that there was no cure for any of the three possible diagnoses. There were no innovative studies taking place, no experimental drugs ready for release, not a glint of hope to clutch.

My only option was to send the remainder of Carol's spinal fluid to the National Prion Disease Pathology Surveillance Center in Cleveland, Ohio, to perform a RT-QuIC test. It was the only lab in the United States that could confirm or eliminate Creutzfeldt-Jakob disease. I asked Dr. Devi to do so. Receiving the results would take six weeks.

Don't Panic! But I Do

That night, lying in bed, my eyes remained wide open. I looked up at the slow-whirring blades of the ceiling fan, and at each full turn, there was a slightly audible click, demanding lubrication. I was too preoccupied to be aggravated by it. I got out of bed and paced the hallway. I heard the blood rushing through my ears—*thump, thump, thump*—and my chest moved double time. The awareness of these sensations heightened my anxiety, which in turn heightened the body sensations. My vision blurred, and the walls narrowed as if I was hallucinating. I was hot and sticky. I instinctively stripped my shirt off and used it to wipe my face, though it was already drenched with sweat. I ran to the bathroom, leaned forward to run cold tap water from the sink into my cupped, trembling hands, and splashed it on my face. I was flooded with adrenaline. I stood straight, and the water traveled from my face to my chest and legs. I felt weak and unsteady, my heart pounded louder and faster, and panic surged through me.

I tried breathing deeply to calm myself, but my breaths were sharp and shallow. I looked around, and my view was a spinning kaleidoscope. *You're dying,* said the voice in my head. Had I not lived most of my life managing panic attacks like the one I was having, I would have been convinced the voice was spot on. I knew the symptoms could take on a life of their own if I didn't manage them, so I put to work a calming method I had used for decades.

I acknowledged the irrational script I was writing, the thoughts single-mindedly centered on the worst that could happen and the feeling of being trapped. I began to breathe deeply with purpose and place awareness on each inhale and exhale. I redirected myself to be in the moment by focusing on my surroundings and said out loud the things around me—a desk, my nightstand, a light switch, etc. I assigned a severity number to my anxiety on a scale from one to ten, and this helped give perspective. Even at my worst I had never been at ten, which helped me realize I could endure more anxiety, which in turn lessened my anxiety. As I reframed my thoughts, the unwanted body sensations slowly faded.

The method was not my invention. It was a blend of advice I'd been given or read over the years. I admit using it can be daunting, as it takes immense effort and concentration to shift from a panicked state to one that is rational, but I relied on my years of experience and knew I'd make it to the other side of an episode.

I was able to return to bed. I slept lightly and woke occasionally. Each time, I turned, looked at Carol in a deep sleep, and wished for the same. The contrast in our temperaments was odd: the one with the terrible diagnosis was in a peaceful state, and the one without it was worried sick.

Adding to my anxiety was the realization that my daughter, Tori, was getting married in five weeks. I thought, *How am I going to pull off a wedding without it being shrouded in sadness?* I noticed my mind darting from concerns over Carol to concerns over shielding Tori and my son, Anthony Jr., from the news until after the wedding.

Finally, rays of light slipped between the shades into our bedroom. An interesting phenomenon happened with my anxieties at daybreak; it was as if the sunrise made them seem smaller and more manageable, and I would wonder why I felt so distraught only moments earlier. I first noticed this when dealing with depression, panic disorder, and agoraphobia at age twenty-five.

My priority this morning was to quiet the storm brewing with Lynn. Out of concern for Carol, she had been asking friends and family for medical advice, and each had their own opinion, some contrary to Dr. Devi's and some in addition to, which seemed equally misplaced. My fear was that as word of Carol's illness spread to family and friends, it would eventually reach Anthony Jr. and Tori, especially given their relationship with cousins who were close to their age. I was afraid they might put a well-intended but devastating post on social media.

After breakfast, I called Lynn and Lee and suggested we all stop discussing the matter with friends, family, and each other. I was doing everything possible for Carol's health, and we needed to prevent a leak that would impact the mood of the upcoming wedding. I also reminded them that the RT-QuIC test results wouldn't be available until after the wedding, so there were no medical decisions that could be made in the interim. Lee and Lynn gracefully agreed to the temporary silence.

We Need a Vacation

I planned a short vacation for Carol, our adult kids, and their future spouses, Gina and Andrew, at Crystal Springs Resort in Sussex County, New Jersey. I knew it might be the last time we could all spend quality time with Carol, and I wanted to take advantage of the opportunity. Everyone loved the idea. There were questions about the need for such a quickly arranged invite, but I put together a rationale that was convincing enough to quiet their curiosity.

We all had fun spending time socializing in the resort's large pool. The kids convinced Carol to slide down the waterslide, and although I sensed her uneasiness, she climbed to the top and let gravity do the rest. At the end of the plunge, we saw a smile that disappeared in a splash and reappeared as a laugh.

I asked if everyone wanted to try out the archery course, and they were quick to agree. Carol told us that she was good at archery when she was young, and everyone's polite response was evidence that we thought it was an overstatement by a mom trying to impress her family. We surrendered our doubt with the speed of the first arrow she released, which hit the bull's-eye. She beat all of us with her final score and more than once.

The Vacation's Over

I had serious matters to deal with at home, the most difficult being meeting with a representative of a cemetery to decide how Carol and I would commemorate our lives. I met with a salesperson for planning purposes. The place was close to our home, and I thought it was proper for our resting place to be near where we had spent the greater part of our lives.

I drove through the unceremonious entryway. There were no wrought iron fences or ornate gates, which seemed practical since there wasn't a sane person trying to break in and certainly no one capable of breaking out. I steered along a winding road past stone angels pitted from age and headstones with names that preserved what bodies could not. My car window was open, and the aromas of cut grass, fresh flowers, and upturned earth were lifted by the summer heat and carried by a breeze into my car. When I was young, I held my breath when driving past a cemetery, a ritual to ward off ghosts from following me home to haunt me.

I parked, and as I headed into the office, I stopped at a monument and read an engraved quote that summarized a person's time on earth, a sad commentary on the no-nonsense ways of life. I touched the concrete slab, and chalky streaks appeared where my fingers had been. There was a stale, metallic tang of stone in the air. Groundskeepers were nearby, pruning trees and shrubs and doing other tasks to ensure an attractive, orderly landscape. One of the men shouted, "Hello!" and I returned the welcoming remark with a nod. I thought a silent gesture was suitable for the sacredness of the surroundings.

As I entered the office, I felt as if I was facing my own mortality as well as Carol's, something I hadn't seriously

Anthony P. Mauro Sr.

thought about and we hadn't discussed. Everything in our lives was changing rapidly, and my immediate response was to jump into action and address the problematic decisions head on. I knew I would need to spend some time in contemplative reflection about our impermanence but hadn't started yet. I was doing things in the wrong order but now had no alternative.

The salesperson presented himself as a businessperson would, complete with a suit, tie, and business card with small print on the backside: *Ask us about our crypts, wall spaces in mausoleums, and outdoor tombs.* His personality was as starched as his shirt. The sales pitch was businesslike, to the point. His briefcase was open on a chair. I couldn't see the contents but half suspected there was a book titled *How to Make a Living Selling Burial Plots.* After an hour of being presented options and a tour of the grounds, I returned home.

I gave Carol a summarized version of my meeting and the requisite brochures, and we ultimately agreed to cremation. I then took her to meet with the same salesperson, and we finalized our arrangements together. I don't know if she fully understood the specifics, but she agreed with my suggestion, and since the arrangements were the same for both of us, I felt comfortable with our decision.

Though I had yet to learn the results of the Creutzfeldt-Jakob test, it was certain Carol had a neurological degenerative disease, so I was better able to recognize symptoms. When she complained that she hated grocery shopping, I had dismissed it as a gripe about doing a mundane chore. I certainly had grumbles about doing routine chores but now realized that she was complaining about putting the grocery list together, not about the chore. I suggested that I go grocery shopping with her, and she seemed relieved.

I soon understood her frustration. At some point, she had decided to use a handheld scanner so that she could register each item as it was placed in the cart. The problem was she didn't know the scanner had a trigger mechanism that needed pulling in order to read the barcode and record the purchase. She wasn't using it correctly, making it impossible to operate. I was so saddened to witness her incapability that my heart sank to the floor.

Another aspect was disheartening. Carol knew where every item was located, because she'd shopped in that supermarket for decades. Now she had difficulty organizing herself to go from aisle to aisle and had to backtrack, and she overlooked some items on the grocery list completely.

As for Tori and Andrew's upcoming wedding, Carol didn't help Tori with the preparations, and she showed no interest in helping with the wedding shower. This should have been a milestone experience for Carol and Tori, a shared journey, a time to reconnect and begin a more adult relationship. This was confusing for all of us and especially upsetting for Tori.

When I relayed Carol's lack of involvement in Tori's wedding to Dr. Devi, she said it might relate to the executive function of the brain. She said that when the area was impacted, a person had trouble starting or finishing tasks, executing multiple steps of a project in sequence, and keeping belongings organized. She added that the person would have difficulty making decisions, might lose important items, and had impulse issues or lack of emotional control.

Doctors, Doctors, and More Doctors

These behavioral changes had driven me to spend one and a half years taking Carol to various doctors, trying to get a diagnosis so we could treat the cause of a growing problem.

I started with her general practitioner, and she performed various tests including one for the thyroid, which might detect an imbalance in the gland's production of hormones, but the results were normal.

I took her to a psychiatrist, who thought it might be mild depression. He determined that medicine wasn't needed and that the condition was temporary. After several months passed and seeing a slight worsening in Carol's unexplainable behaviors, I made an appointment with a local neurologist, thinking that there might be a disorder of the brain and nervous system. The neurologist performed an evaluation to assess her neurological function, muscle strength, nerves, and sensory functions. I was in the room during the evaluation, and though I thought he might have found the reason for Carol's behavioral changes, he said she was fine. I was relieved to hear the results but didn't know where to turn next.

I also researched Carol's symptoms on the internet, trying to match them with medical specialties. It was frustrating, because there weren't physical symptoms like pain that could help in a diagnosis. They were behavioral or psychological in nature. Carol couldn't detect or describe her symptoms.

The fact was that she didn't know she had a medical issue. A few times, I asked her if she noticed any differences with herself, and she paused and said in the sweetest and most convincing voice, "I'm just not on my game." The way she answered was so adorable that it soothed my torment.

By that time, several months had passed, and her unusual behaviors continued. Left with no clear answers, I made another appointment with a psychiatrist. The psychiatrist said it was "atypical depression" and prescribed an antidepressant. I was confused by the diagnosis—having a history with depression, I couldn't see how Carol's symptoms fit. In fact, Carol's general demeanor was upbeat, but he told me he thought her depression would improve. I couldn't imagine what circumstances were causing her depression. I left the office unconvinced and knew intuitively something else was the cause.

I let a few months pass and monitored Carol's behavior to see if there was improvement. Her unusual behavior and poor decision making continued. She didn't keep our home as neat and clean as she used to, which was a major departure from her meticulous nature. She stopped wearing makeup and caring for her hair and nails—also out of character. There was an incident when she brought a urine sample to a laboratory in a Tupperware container instead of using a specimen cup. I didn't notice it until we arrived at the lab.

Tori noticed the changes and described them by saying her mother was "acting childlike." On one occasion, Carol told me she was having difficulty concentrating.

I started calling friends and family to find out if they knew of a neurologist in New York City, and eventually one was recommended.

I was in his office as he performed a neurological evaluation on Carol like the test the neurologist we visited six months earlier had administered. I saw that he looked puzzled with a section of test results. He said her low score could be attributed to anxiety, but to be safe, he referred us to Dr. Devi.

A Few Things about Carol

Between dating and our marriage, I'd known Carol for nearly four decades. Her adorable face was highlighted by an olive skin tone, dark eyes, and silky brown hair, all of which I attributed to her first-generation Italian-American father. Her attractive appearance was classic and timeless.

She had a quiet dignity and was soft spoken, gentle, easygoing, and unassuming, but she asserted herself when necessary. She had a wonderful sense of humor and invented the silliest words, and they were funny because they perfectly fit the situation for which they were conceived.

Carol loved to laugh, though it was more a giggle trying to suppress a full laugh, which increased the vigor of the giggle and amusingly made her shoulders tremble up and down. I enjoyed making her laugh so much that I made it my mission to find every conceivable way to do so.

She grew up in Maplewood, New Jersey, an old community where people sought a break from metro New York City life. The town was a diverse community with a downtown area interchangeably called "the village" or "Maplewood Center." I never learned why some people used one name and not the other, but it didn't distract from the charming storefronts that still had the look of 1950s suburbia.

Carol was raised Catholic, and her faith inspired her to attend a private Jesuit university in Fairfield, Connecticut. The Jesuits were known for cultivating mind, body, and spirit, and she took the lead in instilling the Catholic faith in our family. Throughout our marriage, as she rested her head on the pillow each night, she whispered to me, "I'm going to say my prayers now and fall asleep."

Having lived with her for more than three decades, I would have sworn there was nothing I didn't know about her. Recently I was helping her clean her dresser drawers and found several handwritten prayers on crinkled paper, stuffed between clothing. She spoke to God from her heart, asking to protect our children as they went through difficult challenges in their lives. I read them in a state of awe, empathy, and sadness in view of her medical condition. I wanted so much to be able to talk with her about the prayers, but the capability to express her thoughts had passed.

In the mornings, I'd be in my office and hear her singing in the shower, happy and full of life, her heels thumping to the rhythm of the songs playing in her head. She worked hard at keeping fit and was modest about it. When the kids were small, she started a habit of having family members kiss each other as we left the house and when we went to bed in case life interfered with us seeing each other again.

Carol had a knack for knowing where I had last placed things I was trying to find. She made the coziest beds imaginable, and her talent made me look forward to pulling up the covers each night. She was fastidious about keeping her home neat, her children well dressed, and herself impeccably groomed.

She was so dedicated to our children that she gave up a career in finance at JPMorgan Chase in New York City so she could stay at home and raise them. I remember that a few of her peers tried to make her feel bad about her decision when they chose to remain in the workforce after having children. Carol had such confidence in her choice that she never felt the need to engage in their criticism.

She was good with the little things that could make life feel full. She cooked a great tomato sauce using my grandmother's recipe and baked a scrumptious pumpkin bread that welcomed the fall season into our home. Whether it was the swelter of summer or the chill of winter, when I did chores outside, she always thought of me and brought out a snack and something hot or cold to drink.

Intelligent and honest, she raised our children to ambitious standards and was protective of them. Our values and outlooks on life always aligned. We got through problems by solving them together rather than trying to avoid or argue about them.

Her wonderful nature and character gave me the confidence to propose to her, and never once during our marriage would I have thought to reconsider. She loved her parents and called her mother every night and her sister every Sunday. Polite and mannerly, she respected others and treated them as she wanted to be treated.

I'm not hinting our marriage was perfect, nor am I trying to portray Carol as an angel, but we were well suited to each other, and that is a great foundation for a healthy marriage. I admit that it was easier for me to live with her than the reverse, but neither of us held grudges, and we resolved issues before the day ended. We had mutual respect. We gave each other the benefit of the doubt and were openly affectionate with one another. She understood my offbeat humor and dry delivery. We were best friends.

SEPTEMBER 2018

Tori and Andrew's Wedding

Tori called me, speaking quickly in run-on sentences. I don't remember her pausing to breathe. It was the day before her wedding, and she wanted to go over my responsibilities and start times. She also went over Carol's schedule for makeup, hair styling, bringing her gown to the venue, and a million other details. I listened carefully, mostly for her to hesitate so I could speak, but when there was an opportunity, my attempts were seen as intrusions and met with exasperation. I surrendered to my predicament and remained quiet until she said goodbye and was about to hang up. I wanted to squeeze in a few words of confidence but wasn't quick enough and relayed them to a soulless dial tone.

I felt bad for Tori because her mother couldn't help her plan the wedding. Carol attended all the meetings and venues but did not have decision-making abilities, but she was happy, and that would have to be enough. Tori took it upon herself to arrange the countless preparations that go into weddings. She was heartbroken that her mom wasn't helping, but she knew something was wrong and that I was in the process of getting a diagnosis.

The day of the wedding, Carol and I waited for Tori to arrive at the reception venue in Monmouth Beach, New Jersey. I had grown up in the town and worked here as a waiter during summers while in college more than four decades earlier. At that time, it was a private restaurant, with "Members Only" prominently displayed on the front of the building. Now it was open to the public.

I looked out the second-floor window at the Shrewsbury River and the long docks stretching into the grayish water. When I was a boy, I fished for snapper and eel off the docks and brought them to my grandfather's house on my bike. He'd cook them, and we'd sit over the meal as he told me stories of growing up in the town and his days of fishing in the surrounding water.

During cold spells, the river turned to ice and was transformed into a skating arena. Some fearless teenagers would slap a puck across the smooth, solid surface with L-shaped sticks in impromptu games of hockey and without protective gear, while others used it to show off their skating talent or simply to socialize. The Atlantic Ocean was within eye distance. In the heat of summer, the same kids swam in the cool, salty water and bodysurfed to the sloping shoreline of golden-brown sand.

The borough was one square mile with the ocean on its eastern shore and the Shrewsbury River to the northwest. There were only six hundred people in the town when I was growing up, mostly blue-collar workers living in small, cozy homes on tiny lots. The wealthy lived in Victorian houses with distinct architecture styles that took on lives of their own. It was a sleepy, slow-paced community of friendly characters and personalities that rivaled *The Andy Griffith Show* and the fictional town of Mayberry.

A tourist driving through Monmouth Beach would surely be enchanted. In the heart of town, they'd pass the Corner Store, a place where adults gathered at the counter for a meal, locals talked, and kids passed the time playing pinball. The visitor would likely drive past an elderly, wiry figure pedaling his bike. I never came to know his comings and goings, but I remember that his name was Pete. My grandmother would invite him in for tea, being he was a distant relative of my grandfather. Pete would pour tea from the cup into the saucer and use it to sip from. He repeated the quirky routine until the cup and saucer were empty.

This same tourist might drive past a solitary man living on the river shoreline in a remote area of town called Raccoon Island. His shanty was surrounded by mud and silt from tidal water and large, coarse, common reeds called phragmites. I saw the man only once during the twenty-one years I lived in town; he had a fishing pole in hand as he walked from his home to the nearby river's edge.

While sightseeing, the tourist might stop and see my grandfather at his seafood business in the Galilee section of town. He was part of the colorful history of hardworking Scandinavians who pound fished the ocean. These fishermen rowed heavy boats on the Atlantic waters and lifted pound nets to bring fish to the surface. A team of men scooped the fish out, filled their boats, and then rowed back to the beach where a team of horses on a pulley system dragged the boats ashore, and the fish were offloaded into baskets.

One of my favorite things as a boy was when my father took me to the firehouse. The firetrucks were bigger than I imagined, painted eye-catching red and adorned with ornate gold pinstripes. The noises from these magnificent machines were attention-grabbing bells, whistles, and ear-splitting revving engines. When I entered the building, I was hit by the wonderful smell of rubber from the enormous fire engine tires and neatly folded firehoses. My grandfather and uncle were fire chiefs, and my father was a firefighter and founding member of the first aid squad that shared the building.

The town was run by a mayor, a police chief, and a priest, and when they weren't running the town, helping people, or saving souls, they were arguing baseball as they watched the town kids play the national pastime on a diamond. The left field ended on the mucky banks of Manhasset Creek.

I never understood what added antagonism to their squabbles, but it may have been the splinters they got sitting on the old wooden bleachers. It happened regularly to me. The ballfield was directly across the street from the red brick elementary school that opened its doors in the fall of 1909.

On November 22, 1963, I was eight years old and riding my bike on a dirt road with a friend (only a few hundred yards from where I was standing at Tori's wedding). A man in a parked, heavy GMC truck stopped us and said that President John F. Kennedy had been shot in downtown Dallas. I pedaled home as fast as I could to tell my parents, but the news had already rippled across America and was seared into the American psyche.

I snapped out of my nostalgia, remembering that Carol was standing next to me, also looking out the window of the wedding venue. I didn't know what she was thinking, but she seemed content with whatever it was. I could sense her disorientation with our surroundings; it was slight but perceptible. As we greeted guests and talked with friends, she left some of their polite comments unreturned. She wasn't being rude; I suspect she had difficulty processing the conversation.

For me, it was a day of rippling emotions; happiness for my daughter and her new husband but anxiety over Carol's health and dread over her pending diagnosis. I was caught up in the highs of celebration and then dropped to the lows of watching a mother incapable of being fully present for her daughter's celebration. I made sure that the outside world was clueless to my inner turmoil.

Earlier in the day, my mettle was tested by the convergence of stressors while greeting the groomsmen in the lobby of the hotel. I was sitting in a comfortable chair, waiting for the male half of the bridal party, when the lobby began spinning. I felt like I was losing control over the day, and this created a wave of panic that overwhelmed me and fed on itself, spiraling ever faster and greater. I recognized the start of a panic attack. The sense of terror made me lightheaded. I felt I might keel over every time I stood to greet someone, but I was able to put confidence into every handshake. I did all I could to keep a calm, poised demeanor even though I felt as if I were swarmed by angry hornets after bumping into their nest. I knew that feeling well, having unintentionally disturbed hornets on more than one occasion.

A panic attack had the feeling of imminent death. To make matters worse, it happened as I introduced myself to the arriving guests, but I made sure no one noticed. I was like a high-functioning alcoholic, though my body adapted to compensate for the disruption caused by panic, not booze.

While in the lobby, I used the calming method to diminish the feeling to a manageable level. I made a conscious effort to slow my breathing and redirect my thoughts. I

Anthony P. Mauro Sr.

observed the script I was writing in my mind, which was always catastrophic thinking and fear of losing control.

I assigned my anxiety a severity number on a scale from one to ten. I counted the lobby floor tiles to distract my mind and redirect my attention outward. My anxiety subsided, and I regained a lucid state, but for some reason on this day, it struck me that the calming method I had relied on most of my life was only managing symptoms. It didn't cure the root anxiety. I was tired of living this way and knew the stress of Carol's illness would only make things worse. I made a mental note to find a healthier way to cope, one that would alleviate the cause of the anxiety.

The wedding went flawlessly. Tori looked beautiful in the timeless design of her dress, and Andrew's tuxedo was classic. The atmosphere was euphoric, and they exchanged vows with a beautifully serene river as a backdrop. The forecasted rain held off long enough for the outside ceremony to finish and for everyone to move inside to the grand reception room. I gave my speech as the father of the bride and danced with Tori to Heartland's "I Saw Her First."

Carol was having fun. She laughed and clapped the entire time she was dancing. She was too tired to attend the parties afterward, so we headed home when the wedding ended, but I was grateful for how the day went.

Depression, Panic Disorder, Agoraphobia

I was diagnosed with depression, panic disorder, and agoraphobia forty years ago when I was twenty-five years old. My doctor told me that I would need to accept limitations in life. He said I could expect panic attacks with intense fear, palpitations, sweating, chest pain, shortness of breath, trembling, the feeling of impending doom, and the fear of losing control. According to him, the disorder was biological, caused by imbalances in naturally occurring chemical messengers in the brain called neurotransmitters. Other doctors said that environmental and personality traits were factors too. My experiences made me believe they were a combination of both.

Agoraphobia involved fearing and avoiding places or situations that might cause panic and feelings of being trapped. This fear kept me from wanting to get out into the world. I would get anxious about an actual or upcoming situation such as being in open or enclosed spaces that were unique to me or being in a crowd. My apprehension was caused by the fear that there was no easy way to escape or get help if the anxiety got overwhelming.

At twenty-five, I experienced agoraphobia with my first panic attack, which caused me to worry about having another attack, and then I avoided the place I had the attack, fearing it would happen again. The condition could be so overwhelming that a person might eventually confine themselves to their home.

The moment my doctor finished telling me of the limitations I would have was the moment I refused to accept his prognosis. I don't know if it was defiance, denial, or fear of failure that caused my resolve, but I know it was backed up with steadfast determination. I wouldn't accept a life crippled by anxiety and prevented from accomplishing my goals: a career, marriage, children, and the things that add to a quality life.

Back from the Past: Test Results

The day after Tori's wedding, I thought about the stress that lay ahead, the strain of day-to-day caregiving for Carol, and unforeseeable financial concerns. I wanted to transform myself to accept these uncertainties. After all, they couldn't be controlled. I didn't know how I'd find this equanimity, but I knew there had to be a way. To properly care for Carol, I would have to first care for myself.

Dr. Devi's office called to say she had received the test results, so the following day, Carol and I met with her in New York City. I assumed the worst—that the test was positive for Creutzfeldt-Jakob disease—and assumed Dr. Devi preferred to tell us in person. I did my best to prepare for the words I would hear, how she would say them, and the somberness of the moment. I rehearsed it so I would have no observable reaction that caused Carol concern.

When we entered Dr. Devi's office, her easygoing manner took me off guard, or maybe my state of mind was exceedingly anxious. I didn't have the patience to guess. She motioned for us to sit down, and we chose the seats we had during the first visit. It reminded me of how kids choose to sit in the same seat in a classroom. I thought there must be a psychological basis for this and surprised myself with the ridiculous timing of my thinking. I dismissed it as relieving the dramatic tension in the room. Dr. Devi opened her laptop, studied the screen, looked up at me and Carol, and said that the test was negative for Creutzfeldt-Jakob disease. It took a moment for the words to sink into my mind, but when they did, I felt a wave of relief. The wave quickly crashed.

She continued, "Carol has an incurable brain condition called frontotemporal degeneration." Since FTD was discussed during our first meeting, I had taken the time to research it before our appointment. I listened to Dr. Devi's description for as long as my concentration allowed, since

I was still distressed by the news. Dr. Devi said that FTD brought a gradual, progressive decline in behavior, language, or movement with memory relatively preserved in most cases. The onset usually occurred between the ages of forty-five and sixty-four. She paused, and I did a quick mental assessment. Carol's symptoms started around fifty-seven, but they could have been earlier.

She went on to tell me that FTD was frequently misdiagnosed as Alzheimer's disease, depression, Parkinson's disease, or a psychiatric condition. On average it took 3.6 years to have it diagnosed, so I felt fortunate that Carol was diagnosed after one and a half years of pinballing between doctors. She prepared me by saying I would observe increasing difficulty in Carol's ability to plan and organize activities. Dr. Devi presented the diagnosis in more supportive and reassuring terms than my pragmatism allowed.

As I absorbed the diagnosis, I turned to Carol to console her. She was eerily unemotional and asked Dr. Devi if FTD was Alzheimer's disease. Dr. Devi replied politely that Carol did not have Alzheimer's disease, as she had mentioned during our last office visit.

Carol was satisfied and proclaimed she was ready to go home. Her words only added to the surrealness of the moment, but I credited her lack of understanding to being a symptom of FTD and was grateful that she couldn't concern herself with the gravity of the diagnosis.

As soon as we arrived home, I did more research on FTD, since the diagnosis was now definitive. I reread much of the information that Dr. Devi had provided and was again thrown into the depths of disbelief. I remembered Dr. Devi showing me an MRI of Carol's brain and saying that the neurodegenerative disorder was associated with shrinkage of the frontal and temporal anterior lobes. Even my untrained eye saw noticeable shrinkage.

There were different types of FTD, and Carol had the behavioral variant. People with the behavioral variant had behavior changes, disinhibition, apathy, and loss of empathy, and they ate too much food or inedible things. I had already begun to hide food, particularly sweets, in cabinets to keep it from Carol. It would become routine, especially during the first few years of the illness, since compulsive behavior is common with FTD. Her impulsivity would have her eating substantial amounts of food if left to her own doing.

The average length of survival of those with FTD was seven years from its onset, and there were no treatments to stop the progression.

Dr. Devi treated behavioral symptoms with behavior modification and medications for restlessness, agitation, and other behaviors. She recommended a therapy called transcranial magnetic stimulation (TMS), a noninvasive procedure believed to improve cognitive performance of people with FTD. I scheduled Carol for weekly treatments.

Telling the Kids

A few days after Tori's wedding, I sat in my home office with my phone in hand to ask Anthony Jr. and Tori to meet me and tell them what I had learned about their mom's illness. Almost six weeks had passed since we were told Carol had Creutzfeldt-Jakob, FTD, or Lewy body dementia, so I had time to prepare myself emotionally.

Since they thought whatever was happening to their mother was treatable, my call would arouse curiosity but not dire concern. I felt the enormous weight of having to tell them news that would forever change their lives, but my background in business had prepared me for difficult conversations, so I organized a narrative around the facts of FTD and was prepared to discuss some of the ways it might affect our lives. I would reinforce my support with the promise to help navigate uncertainties and readiness to listen and answer questions. I wasn't going to sugarcoat the reality of the situation but would deliver the news with the assurance that whatever the future had in store for us, we would face it together.

I placed calls to both of them, and by mid-afternoon, they were sitting with me in my office. I explained the diagnosis, and though they had seen changes in their mother and knew something was wrong, they weren't prepared to hear it was a form of dementia. The news hit them hard, and I worked to help them with their shock, disbelief, and fear, which finally gave way to anguish and tears. Their reactions were deeply painful. It took every effort to focus my attention on them and not consider my own agony.

After composing themselves, they went to see their mom in the family room where she was watching TV. I could hear them making small talk, and after thirty minutes, they left for their homes. I watched their cars exit the driveway from my office window, feeling guilt over changing their worlds, and the fact that I was only the messenger was no consolation. I stayed at the window long after they were gone. It was nearing the middle of September, and I thought about prior years standing there enjoying the landscape of trees turning reds, rich deep burgundies, coppery oranges, and golden yellows. The colors brought warmth and comfort to the season, but I knew the splendor would now be wasted on me. It was a melodramatic moment, but I indulged it.

Anthony P. Mauro Sr.

I turned my thoughts to how I could help my kids cope as I made my way through my own grief.

I called Lee and Lynn and told them of the diagnosis. They were also relieved that it wasn't Creutzfeldt-Jakob disease. Lynn suggested that Carol participate in trials, see other doctors, and try anecdotal cures, but there was no hope for an immediate cure, and trials would mean major disruptions to Carol's life with little or no likelihood of success. I knew that the best we could do was manage the progression of the disease.

In the weeks that followed, I immersed myself in learning more about FTD. I found out there was a strong genetic component, though no one in the family remembered anyone having it. (Carol's mother had Alzheimer's disease, a different form of dementia that didn't become evident until she was in her eighties.) My kids were aware of the possible genetic link and talked to me about it.

I learned from Dr. Devi that research was ongoing and clinical trials and studies predicted breakthrough medicines. Even though nothing could cure FTD, there was a good chance that medicines to treat it would be available before Anthony Jr. and Tori reached ages of concern.

Anthony Jr. called one afternoon and asked what I thought of him having a genetic test that could identify FTD in his DNA; Tori called a few days later and asked the same. I had thought that they would ask, so I was ready for their questions. I understood their concern and appreciated that genetic testing was an individual choice, so I presented the pros and cons so they could decide for themselves.

Whether positive or negative, the test results can provide a sense of relief for some people. It gives them a chance to make informed decisions about healthcare, finances, having kids, and other life decisions. It can even make them aware of new therapies or experimental treatments. For other people, a positive result for FTD can cause negative emotions and social or financial worries. They might feel depression, anger, anxiety, and guilt about the results, and this might unnecessarily impact their decision to have children. Having a positive test result might make it difficult to get life insurance, long-term care insurance, or long-term disability insurance.

There are also some limitations to genetic testing. Some of the genes associated with FTD are known but not all of them, so the possibility of ruling out FTD isn't 100 percent. Plus, genetic testing can't determine if a person will show symptoms, at what age symptoms might begin, the severity of the symptoms, or how quickly the symptoms will progress.

Carol and I raised our children to think for themselves. Life isn't black and white, and often the options we have available don't guarantee the desired outcome. We gave them the pros and cons of issues along with our opinions, let them choose the direction they thought was best, and learned from the results. At the right age, I think this approach is valuable. It's taking off the training wheels from life. I warned the kids that the challenge of being a free thinker is the high price people make you pay for it. It is a form of open-mindedness, a willingness to question assumptions and conclusions, to understand the world on their own terms rather than accept what they are told. My experience has been that people prefer their assumptions and conclusions and get cranky when their beliefs are challenged.

Anthony Jr. and Tori decided not to have the test performed.

Carol's Retirement

Carol worked in the financial department for the township of Colts Neck for eighteen years, managing fiscal affairs. She started working again when our kids were in middle school and I was operating a home-based business. The fact that I was home allowed our kids to always have a parent available when they returned from school.

The town was a bedroom community in Central New Jersey, located within the New York metropolitan area and close to the beaches of the Jersey shore. It was originally a farming community, and though there had been land development, approximately one thousand acres had been preserved, which helped to stem expansion. The town was known for horse farms, and many still exist.

I moved the family to Colts Neck because it was one of the few places left in Monmouth County with open space. It wasn't overly developed due to strict zoning ordinances and the use of well water and septic systems. After living in towns dotted by houses on postage stamp-sized lots with rows of driveways lining streets, I found privacy a welcome relief.

I got to know Carol's boss, John, over the eighteen years she worked for him. Given Carol's FTD diagnosis, I called to see if he had noticed changes in her work performance. He was a pragmatic fellow, the type you would expect to oversee a town's finances. Carol liked him, and I imagined it was because he cared about his employees. People gravitate toward people who treat them well, and I think they flee when not treated fairly. He told me that she had always been his best employee, but during the past year, she was increasingly making mistakes. Carol managed the town's payroll, and when the slipups were in people's paychecks, even the shyest prepared to do battle when they found they had been underpaid. To compound matters, Carol's blunders were high profile. John said the mistakes had become a problem.

The next day, I casually asked Carol when she was thinking of retiring, and she said she was ready. I encouraged her to stop working and sensed her relief. Her coworkers had a retirement party for her a few months later. She must have been feeling lost and overwhelmed at work. I felt terrible for not knowing it.

Medicines, Speech Therapy, and TMS

Carol was prescribed a regimen of medicines and vitamins—a selection that would help with her declining memory, reasoning, and language. They would also manage agitation, restlessness, mood, and irritability, but none of the prescriptions and over-the-counter treatments were cures.

Dr. Devi also recommended speech and language therapy to slow the decline of her language ability and to compensate for losses over time. She warned me that some professionals might find ways to avoid treating Carol. Some speech and language therapists preferred patients with the potential for measurable improvement, and since this wasn't possible with FTD patients, they would eventually give a reason for ending therapy.

I found this to be true with the first language therapy practice I used. It was affiliated with a hospital, and after only three months, I was told they could no longer use the medical billing code for Carol's treatment. I was forced to find a different provider, and to Dr. Devi's point, the new language therapy practice submitted and was reimbursed for the medical billing codes that the first practice said couldn't be used.

Dr. Devi also recommended transcranial magnetic stimulation (TMS). She spent time discussing the benefits of this noninvasive method of brain stimulation that applied magnetic fields to specific areas. The device operated outside the body and didn't require anesthesia. Dr. Devi was one of the few neurologists using the technique with FTD patients, and she emphasized that it wasn't a cure but had promising results with language performance.

I did research on TMS. Because its use in FTD patients was in the initial stages, there wasn't much information available, but there was enough to confirm Dr. Devi's medical opinion. This information and her recommendation gave me the confidence to go ahead with weekly treatments for Carol.

Dr. Devi's accomplishments were impressive. Equally impressive was the number of famous people I met in the waiting area, including a musician, a TV personality, a social leader, a broadcast journalist, and a singer. Others I met were not famous but traveled from all over the world to seek her advice and care.

During one of our visits, I was sitting in the waiting area, reading work-related email, while Dr. Devi was with Carol. I was oblivious to the person in the chair next to me, too focused to care that his elbow was lightly pressed against mine. When Carol left the exam room, I got up to greet her, and when I turned to reach for the exit doorknob, I found myself nose to nose with the legendary singer Tony Bennett. I realized it had been his elbow touching mine. Tony Bennett went public with his diagnosis of Alzheimer's disease in a segment of *60 Minutes,* and Dr. Devi was featured as his neurologist.

OCTOBER 2018

FTD and Me

It is easy to be confused, overwhelmed, and lost when it comes to understanding and choosing treatments and approaches for a rare disease in a loved one, and FTD is no different. Dr. Devi told me there are only sixty thousand reported cases of FTD in the United States.

The normality of my life was changing quickly. I had spent more than sixty years planning my future, advancing through school, building a career, raising a family, growing my business, developing hobbies, and looking for the next thing to capture my attention. Thoughts about my mortality or my wife's were drowned out by ambitions and daily living.

I was unprepared for the downward curveball that life had pitched, and it had me reeling. I exercised nearly every day of my adult life, and I continued going to the gym. I knew it was important to help relieve stress and provide some resilience to depression, which was a concern given my history, so I kept to my routines and maintained a sense of humor, at least publicly.

Anthony P. Mauro Sr.

I was waking at my normal hour of 5:00 a.m., but it was a fight to get out of bed in the month after the diagnosis. I didn't want to move, my mind was overwhelmed, and I felt raw and exposed by the thought of throwing off the covers. I exercised in a mental fog on autopilot. Planning the day, showering, and putting on clothes took effort. I was going through the motions of everyday activities.

I had dealt with major depression, but I was concerned that the current stress might trigger a relapse along with recurring panic attacks. I also knew I needed to be mentally present for my wife and kids, and this added pressure. I had trained myself to live with the panic attacks and anxiety using the calming method, but I had never experienced this degree of anguish.

I understood that FTD worsened over time, that it was life shortening and brought about many changes I would need to adjust to including being a caregiver for Carol. I couldn't think of all the changes that lay ahead, and trying to imagine them only increased my anxiety. I felt isolated and alone.

Despite my preoccupation, I could see that trying to find ways to hide from the collecting storm would be self-defeating, a form of sticking my head in the sand. Again, I thought that I needed to change at a core level. I wanted to live free of anxiety, to awaken to life and learn to live it as it is, but I was suffering because it wasn't what I wanted it to be. I wanted to be *willing* to live as life is. I could not wait on God.

Don't Take the Train

We were making weekly visits to New York City for Carol's TMS treatments, and we met with Dr. Devi monthly. We took the same train each time, and I felt I had a good understanding of the limits of Carol's abilities.

One day, on our way to our appointment, we arrived early at the station, and while waiting on the platform, I noticed the sky sagging with dark, gloomy clouds. Since we had twenty minutes before the train's arrival, I told Carol that I would run back to the car, about a hundred yards from us in the parking lot, to get an umbrella. Before I left, I reminded her to stay seated on the bench and I'd be right back. She assured me she would, and I knew she would be in view the entire time as I ran to the car and back.

I had just grabbed the umbrella when I turned to see a train pulling into the station. I was stunned. I knew that our train wasn't expected then and couldn't imagine it arriving twenty minutes early. Though Carol had told me she would stay seated until I returned, I sprinted to the platform. When I arrived, the train doors had shut, and the conductor had motioned the engineer to depart. The bench where I had left Carol was empty, and the train was slowly gathering momentum as it headed for the next stop.

I don't know how many thoughts a mind can hold in one instant, but it seemed like mine held hundreds when fueled by adrenaline. I thought of every scenario Carol might face when arriving in the middle of the complex and byzantine layout of Penn Station without me. It was as if I was watching a child make their way into the danger of highway traffic, knowing I couldn't get to them in time to save them. My imagination was in overdrive and putting as much strain on my heart as the mad rush back to the platform. I was frantic and wide eyed.

Fortunately, the conductor saw my panicked demeanor through the window of the closed door. He opened the door and waved to the engineer, and the locomotive came to a stop.

As the conductor was stepping onto the platform, I explained that my wife had boarded and she had dementia. I gave her name. I think I finished explaining my dilemma before he finished taking his step. The train stretched for as far as my eye could see, and I realized we might have to search each car. I didn't know if he would keep the train stopped as long as necessary. My fear clouded rational thinking. I watched the conductor open a panel, grab a microphone, and page Carol to exit the train. The sound system was full of fuzzy static, pops, and crackles, and his words were so unclear that I thought Carol would never understand that she was being summoned. The situation felt hopeless. With the casual stride of a walk in a park, Carol stepped from the open door in front of me. My shoulders slumped with relief. This was an earlier train that had rolled into the station, not the one we had been waiting for.

I asked Carol if she heard me say to wait on the bench until I returned. She said yes, and that was the end of the explanation. She wasn't aware of the possibilities or consequences of going into the largest American metropolis alone or that she had left me behind. I realized that she would need eyes on her from that moment forward.

Ecology and Consciousness

On another occasion, we were arriving at Secaucus Junction. I was certain of it because of Carol's announcement. I was looking out the window at the Meadowlands. Most people might recognize the name for the location of the stadium used by the Giants and Jets, but more importantly, at least from an ecological viewpoint, the expanse was a mosaic of swamps, marshes, and wetland habitat. It was also the station before our final stop, Penn Station.

My imagination got the better of me, and I remembered a conversation with Len, a professor emeritus of wildlife ecology and management at Rutgers University. Len was a friend and an officer of a statewide conservation organization I had founded. He said that hundreds of years ago, the Meadowlands was comprised of Atlantic white cedar swamps, salt marshes, and upland habitat. Today, it is a system of fragmented urban wetlands speckled with dumps and a lattice of railroads, bridges, highways, pipelines, and dikes, and it is bordered by residential, industrial, and commercial development.

Despite the manufactured structures that degraded the ecosystem, it remains home to shore birds, waterfowl, and other animals. It is a breeding ground for fish, animals, and plant life. Each human imposition, as well intended as it may be, interrupts ecosystems of food, migration and travel routes, fertile soils, and refuges with flooding, land degradation, and disease. We have valued these lands in terms of dollars, not in terms of environmental health and sustainability, which enriches us in one way and robs us in another.

The reason I focused on ecology at this stop, and admittedly on many of our train rides to New York, was that I was drawn by the idea that a consciousness flowed through living things in ecosystems, a force that sustains a needed balance in the lives of inhabitants. As each living thing goes about their business, they are unaware they are creating the whole of an ecosystem, and to remove or compromise one thing is to undermine the whole.

I had the sense that the same consciousness that flowed through and moved the natural world was a force that moved the human world too, even more so due to our brain's unique capability for higher awareness. I was intrigued by the idea that connecting to this consciousness could provide me with a spiritual transformation that could alleviate my anxieties. I believed it was an avenue to pursue, putting me a step closer to my goal of finding a method to achieve it.

The train lurched forward, bringing me back to the present. The car was full of people, standing room only. The man next to me couldn't find a seat and was trying to hold himself steady by grabbing an overhanging bar as the train moved side to side, making its way along rails that eased into a ninety-degree bend. He bumped into me, and the end of his umbrella stuck into my thigh. He nervously apologized.

An umbrella stab was the only other interesting feature of the trip to the doctor's office. I describe the rest of the afternoon as having the magic of an ordinary day. Nothing new happened, nothing being defined in the most material sense as a lack of anything odd occurring. I was okay with it. In fact, I welcomed it.

A Look Inside My Head

I am aware that my thinking can be seen as unconventional. A few of my close friends call me "eccentric" and less polite things, but we've remained friends for more than sixty years, so I can't be too unusual. Besides, no one stands out by trying to fit in.

When I was a baby, my mother would use a purple drinking cup made of aluminum to pour warm water over my head to rinse shampoo from my hair, using the kitchen sink as a tub. About fifty years later, I was sitting over a Thanksgiving meal with my family and said to my parents,

"During my baptism, I have a vague memory of the priest pouring water on my forehead, because in my mind, it was like he was using the purple cup to rinse my hair in the sink." They smiled politely. I continued, "I also associate intense fear with that moment. I felt like I was choking." My parents' disbelief was expected, since I was only three months old when baptized, but I insisted and repeated the story despite their murmurs of incredulity.

After the second telling, my father turned to my mother and said, "You told him."

My mother responded, "I told him what?"

He said, "You told him what happened during his baptism!"

She shot back, "How could I have told him what happened during his baptism since I had to stay home and wasn't there?"

My father turned to back to me. "Yeah, something happened when the priest poured water over you. I think it got into your mouth and nose and made you choke."

I don't blame my parents, or anyone else, for their disbelief. Even scientific literature suggests that it's not possible to have a memory from before the age of two, but my father confirmed my memory of fear and choking as the water poured on me. The story seems unbelievable.

Heightened perception has been with me all my life. It has helped me to control and evaluate emotions and understand the emotions of others, but I think it has been a double-edged sword. While it keeps me attuned to the wonders of life, it has also made me susceptible to emotional pains that were too overwhelming to wisely cope with in my early years. It caused a reactive and unhealthy response to life challenges. I'd stuff and lock the pain into an emotional pressure cooker until it could no longer contain the force. At twenty-five, it erupted into depression, panic disorder, and agoraphobia. There was likely a biological/chemical component too, but there is no question in my mind that environmental and developed personality traits aggravated it.

The next indelible memory with fear came at the age of four. It was overpowering. I couldn't identify it at the time, but in later years, I came to know it was panic. It happened as I stood next to my mother on the sidewalk, waiting for a bus. An old, faded-yellow 1940s school bus rounded the corner of Wesley Street and stopped in front of our home. My mother lifted and placed me on the lowest step and patted my back to prompt me inside. I turned and protested but got no sympathy as the folding doors pressed together, clipping the tip of my nose. As I found my seat and looked through the window, I saw my mother waving goodbye. A nervousness stewed in my stomach, and when the bus began moving, it surged through me. It was the first dose of anxiety I remember, and I remember it for its intensity. I had never felt such anxiety before and didn't know what to do with it. I was embarrassed and feared the other kids might notice it, so I instinctively stuffed it into an emotional hole and put a cover over it.

I was heading to Seashore Day Camp, a recreational program where kids learned to swim and play together during the summer. It was only a few miles from my home, and I suspect the reason my parents enrolled me had less to do with recreation and more to do with giving my mother a reprieve from managing me as she cared for my one-year-old brother.

I did my best to ignore my anxiety throughout the day. I didn't know what to do with it, but as the day progressed, the anxiety grew. I feared not knowing which of the buses lined up outside of the camp would take me home, if I would miss it entirely, or if I'd get on the wrong bus and never see my family. Camp counselors were strangers and didn't seem approachable, and I had no idea what was expected of me. I felt increasingly powerless throughout the day.

Seashore Day Camp was a lovely place to be, and I was fortunate for the opportunity, but my perception of fear was the lens through which I viewed reality. It was what I focused on, understood, and interpreted, and the result was anxiety. I was too young to come up with a good coping mechanism for my inner mayhem, so I did what came naturally: I crammed my angst down deep enough to make room for a lifetime more.

I don't know if this was the exact moment I developed this unhealthy coping mechanism, but it is my earliest memory of it. I used repression often, and it worked wonderfully into adulthood, or so I thought.

Home Base

As life would have it, plenty of fuel was thrown on my anxiety fires, and I used my stuff-it-down technique daily. The atmosphere in my home while growing up was unpredictable and chaotic, which triggered intense "fight or flight" fear in me. My father was tough on me and my brothers in an idealistic way but by today's standards would be considered harsh and abusive. He was a bull in a shop, and we were china. I couldn't process these stressors as a kid, so I repressed the adrenaline-charged fear and confusion all the time. A doctor had told me that the brain drives the "fight or flight" response and release of stress hormones and that children have a limited capacity to manage this kind of stress. Such adversity can lead to lifelong problems.

It's not my purpose to assign blame for the conditions in my life or see myself as a victim, but I feel it's important to understand my reactions if I'm to try to unlearn them, and ridding myself of the cause of the anxiety remains a goal. There was one benefit to the "fight or flight" home environment: I decided not to allow myself to be defeated by it and was determined to overcome my adversity. This willpower developed into an invaluable tool for achievements in my adult life.

There was no question that my parents loved me and my two brothers. My father worked two or three menial jobs weekly to provide for our family, and my mother stayed home to raise her kids. We had one breadwinner and were a low-income family for my first twelve years of life. My parents did their best under stressful circumstances, and I was fortunate to have a roof over my head and food on the table. I'm not a perfect parent, so I don't hold my parents to a higher standard.

Understanding my background, the environment, and the development of my personality traits provides a backdrop of the core aspects I was sure I would need to help me unravel a bird's nest of impossibly tangled neurons. The neural networks that I had formed were the mechanism that tamped unwanted emotions into a finite reservoir of anxiety. It became a pattern that I believe is part of the foundation of my panic disorder, depression, and agoraphobia. Understanding the convoluted systems I designed to deal with trauma and unwanted emotions is useful in my healing.

For as long as I can remember, I felt anxious, constantly worrying about something happening or trying to avoid something that might happen. The result was a state of heightened fear, which was implicated in a range of anxiety disorders.

More Noteworthy Events

I was nine years old when my friend invited me to go ocean fishing. His father had recently bought a boat, and since I had fished in rivers for many years, the prospect of doing it in the ocean was exciting, a new adventure. I was surprised at the invitation, because I found his father to be aloof and no-nonsense, which wasn't a bad thing, but to me, it was intimidating.

The boat was docked on the river, and it was a forty-five-minute ride along a stretch of channel to the mouth of the ocean. I was having fun with my friend and watching people going about their business along the embankments. Some got their enjoyment casting fishing lines with one hand while flicking cigarette ashes with the other, while others got theirs being spectators. I didn't understand how they had discovered the fishing area; it seemed the envy of all little-visited destinations.

We made our way along the channel and into the bay. It was a wide opening and stocked with passing pleasure boats and their colliding wakes. As we approached the mouth of the ocean, a familiar fear started to sweep over me. The nearer we got to the ocean, the more the fear was magnified. Finally, we began a turn around a thin peninsula called Sandy Hook, and as we crossed what I believed to be the demarcation between bay and ocean, I did the same between calm and panic. It was unexpected and inexplicable, and I was paralyzed. I didn't know what was happening, but it had an eerie familiarity. I didn't draw the parallel to the Seashore Day Camp bus incident, but I recognized it on some level. Every instinct was telling me to flee, but I was trapped in a boat surrounded by water, which intensified the panic.

The ocean waters were angrier than those of the bay. I had never experienced it before. I was convinced I was nauseous, though to this day, I don't know if this was real or imagined. Such considerations didn't matter, because I panicked and wanted to get out of the boat. I knew my friend's father was looking forward to fishing and just spent forty-five minutes to get to this spot, and I felt caught between my growing anxiety and being intimidated by him.

The mind is a complex and inventive thing, and mine was about to make use of its ingenuity. On a subconscious level, I was embarrassed to show my fear to others and equally embarrassed to use fear as an excuse to ruin their plans, so I blurted, "I feel sick. I'm going to throw up."

Surprisingly, my strategy to escape by playing on sympathy, or betting on my friend's dad not wanting me to puke on his newly waxed gunnels, worked wonderfully. His grumbling was understandable, and it continued for most of the forty-five-minute ride back to the dock. I was too focused on the relief I felt and hadn't regained enough composure to give his frustration due consideration. I wasn't surprised that I was never invited to go fishing again, but I had no desire to ask.

I didn't dwell on the cause of the anxiety or why it started as we entered the ocean. It never rose from the subconscious to the conscious. I was young and unaware of the complexities of the psyche, and I knew I had avoided catastrophe—an imagined catastrophe, no doubt—but that was my only consideration. It was one more layer of adrenaline-filled emotion stuffed into my emotional dump-ster that would eventually erupt into a calamitous fire, but not on this day. This day was a fun boat ride, at least on the trip home.

I was a sophomore in high school the next time I was overwhelmed by anxiety. I had just finished eating six McDonald's hamburgers and two bags of fries and washed them down with a milkshake. I was trying to put meat on my skinny frame so I could compete in the upcoming football season. I was very self-conscious about my weight.

I was with friends, and we were driving along a stretch of highway that hugged the Jersey shore. I was in the back seat of a two-door car with two other guys. Pressed shoul-der to shoulder, I felt trapped in the confined space, and it triggered panic to flee the car. My heart was pounding, my breathing quickened, my muscles tensed, and beads of sweat appeared on my face. I kept my internal havoc to myself, self-conscious that if my friends knew of my fear, their teasing would have been too embarrassing to bear. I managed the overwhelming anxiety the way I had taught myself: repressing it and adding another layer on the other compressed emotions. The panic spiraled, and my mind raced with catastrophic thinking, and the more my thoughts raced, the more the panic spiraled, feeding on itself. I felt helpless to stop it.

I wasn't thinking rationally, or I would have asked the driver to pull the car to the curb so I could get out. I felt the contents of my stomach rising, so I rolled down the rear window as quickly as I could, stuck my head out, and retched as we sped down the highway. I blamed it on food poisoning to save face with my friends, and they bought the excuse, which made their teasing bearable.

As impossible as it seems, I wasn't conscious of my anxiety at that point in my life. It seemed subconscious, a sense of nervousness running as background noise. I didn't realize I was always "on edge" even when I had nothing to worry about, because I didn't know any other mental state. I had nothing to compare it to and assumed that what I felt was the same for everyone.

The next incident happened when I was a junior, playing on the high school varsity football team. I had felt a sense of sadness for some time but couldn't pinpoint a reason. I had lost interest in playing, and it affected my performance. I had difficulty concentrating, which was an issue for as long as I could remember, but it was prevalent during this period.

The team was off to a terrible season, and the coaches were extremely frustrated, especially the head coach. He was an overweight guy with bulging forearms like the cartoon character Popeye. An intimidating figure for sure, he looked grumpy even when smiling. He grew a five o'clock shadow well before noon and talked out of one side of his mouth as if gritting his teeth on an invisible cigar. He was working us much harder than usual, an act of frustration born of our poor performance. He became exasperated with our uselessness and demanded that everyone stay late to continue drills until he saw improvement.

I was already mentally overwhelmed, probably clinically depressed but didn't know it at the time, and the first thought after hearing we had to stay late was that I'd miss the last bus home. Missing the bus was an inconvenience to most kids, but the thought made me feel trapped and anxious, and the more I thought about it, the more trapped I felt. The intensity of my anxiety was such that I heard my heart thumping inside my football helmet. We were being pushed harder through several football drills and told we'd remain on the field until the last one of us performed perfectly. All I could think of was missing the bus, being trapped, and feeling paralyzed by anxiety. I got through football practice without anyone knowing my inner turmoil.

I was able to mask the anxiety and panic in social settings so that no one knew what was occurring, but this was bought with repression of feelings, and the layers of repression were a high-piling debt. I constructed a dysfunctional life by avoiding my limitations but wasn't conscious of it. I was an emotional cripple. The chronic repression of my feelings while growing up in a fight-or-flight environment was starting to make me feel isolated and melancholy. Plus, there was the biological/chemical component. I wasn't much of a student—not that I didn't have potential, but difficulty with concentration had always made studying a challenge.

During this period, I had to take the Scholastic Aptitude Test (SAT) in preparation for college, and my concentration was so poor that after trying to answer the first few questions, I couldn't continue, or didn't want to, and I penciled in my answers without reading the questions. I did the same the second time I took the SAT but told myself I would finish the entire test on the third and final attempt. On my last chance to take it, I gave it my best, but halfway through, I could no longer concentrate, and like before, penciled in the answers without reading the questions. Fortunately, my score was good enough to get me into college.

The sadness and feelings of isolation lifted a little in my senior year. I was able to apply myself, and my concentration improved, and for the first time, I made the honor roll for the year.

Off to College...Kinda

Attending college also stressed my poor coping skills. The college was only a one-hour drive from my home. Home was a psychological refuge, and the feeling of not being able to access it when I wanted made me panicky, but I still wasn't fully conscious of the underlying anxiety.

I lived on the campus with the sense of impending doom that if I couldn't get home on any given weekend, something terrible would happen. (Subconsciously, the impending doom was a panic attack.) For some reason, going home every weekend allowed me to avoid the feeling of being trapped. Why I could compartmentalize five days per week and make the feelings tolerable but couldn't on the weekends, I'll leave to professionals to determine. It was a mystery to my mind, but I did it until I graduated.

Agoraphobia and panic disorder have medical definitions, and the symptoms were how I lived my life. Agoraphobia made me avoid places or situations that would bring on a sense of feeling trapped, which resulted in having a panic attack. Some places or situations were trivial, like a movie theater or restaurant table, where I avoided feeling trapped by choosing the seat closest to the aisle or exit. A few times while working as a waiter, the maître d' asked me to stay later than my shift, and for reasons I couldn't explain, this brought a feeling of being trapped. I always came up with an excuse to leave.

The Gift That Keeps Giving

Other places that caused me to feel trapped were more understandable, like flying on a plane or entering an elevator.

One time, I boarded a plane in a driving rainstorm. The flight was full, and I was in a middle seat in the rear of the plane. The people on each side of me were overweight, and their bodies pressed against mine. After the flight attendant closed the cabin door, I started to feel panicked, but there was nothing I could do to exit the cramped fuselage. The plane taxied to another area where it remained while waiting for the weather to clear. As I started to panic, the narrow fuselage got narrower. The bodies to the left and right of me felt closer, their skin bearing down on mine. The plane sat on the tarmac for two hours before taking off. For years after this incident, I avoided flying.

I had yet to experience what would become recurrent and unexpected periods of intense anxiety and panicked sensations that made my heart pound so hard and fast I thought it would burst. I had yet to experience the disorientation and lightheadedness or the feeling that I was going out of my mind.

After I graduated college, I lived with my parents for a brief period and then moved in with a friend. My anxiety seemed less evident, probably because there was less stress in my life. I didn't have a mortgage, family, or other obligations, but in hindsight, it may have been an arranged independence so I could avoid feeling confined by responsibilities. The structure I created for my mental world was a house of cards on the verge of collapse.

My Calling

I wasn't sure what I was doing with my life. I graduated with a teaching degree, and while I knew it wasn't the career for me, I found nothing else remotely interesting. I worked as a waiter while pursuing a short-lived singing career, but this too wasn't my calling.

Anthony P. Mauro Sr.

It was a period when I read books on mysticism with insights into spiritual truths. I took a few courses in The Sedona Method, an easy-to-learn technique to let go of painful, unwanted feelings. Mysticism and The Sedona Method played a key role in seeding an anxiety cure that would blossom forty-five years later, but at that moment, pragmatism prevailed, and I wanted to find something I would love to do for a living.

I called a friend who was an attorney, an affable guy I knew from my hometown, and invited him to lunch to learn about law as a career, but by the end of our meeting, I had heard enough. It was as interesting as terrible music. Just before we finished our meal, he told me about a master of business administration program he had enrolled in but eventually found wasn't of interest. Once he finished describing the key aspects of the degree including management, leadership, and entrepreneurship, I had an aha moment. I knew I had found my purpose and enrolled in graduate school. Interestingly, when I was an undergraduate, I had considered business as a major, but it seemed dry and boring. Sometimes we find what we aren't looking for before we find we are looking for it.

About this time, I reconnected with an old friend. Eventually we became roommates and then bought rental property together. He was a good man, a good friend, and had a talent for working with pencils that left trails of graphite numbers in their wakes, a skill that served him well as an accountant. He was a black-and-white fellow, seeing the world in terms of debits and credits, and he ran his life as if it were organized by the lines on a ledger sheet.

His skill was the reason I bought two homes on a piece of property with him. We rented out the front home. In the rear of the property was the cottage that we lived in, though it was barely more than a shed: two tiny bedrooms, a ten-by-ten living area, a walk-in kitchen, and a small bathroom. As my grandfather used to say, our living space was "tighter than a clam's ass"—way too tight for bachelor living.

I had started working as a sales representative for a food brokerage company that represented food manufacturers. I spent my days driving to supermarkets and making sure our products were purchased, stocked, and displayed prominently. I attended graduate school in the evenings. My work responsibilities and college studies were stressful, but I wasn't aware of the toll they were having on me. My first week on the job, I trained with an older salesperson, and I was a passenger in his car as we drove to different sales stops on his schedule. He put the air conditioning fan on its highest speed, and I lowered the speed—not because I was cold or it blew too strong but because I was misdirecting my anxiety. I must have felt trapped in the car with him. My tampering with the fan setting didn't agree with him, and he hastily returned it to the highest setting.

I wasn't aware of feeling trapped at the time, but I see it in retrospect. I'm not sure what he thought about my eccentricity with the fan setting, but he seemed to mistakenly think I was challenging his ownership of the vehicle when really it was a tragic symptom of my desperation. I can't say I blamed him.

About a year later, I was driving to a party with a few friends, and as we arrived, I felt extremely nervous about entering the house. I also felt nauseous, so I dropped off my friends and went to a nearby pharmacy to buy something to soothe my stomach. I returned to the party but was uneasy

Anthony P. Mauro Sr.

the entire time, and I kept asking myself why I wasn't having a good time, as everyone else seemed to be.

The Big One

Within days of the incident, I was making my first sales call of the morning at a nearby supermarket and going through the routines of the job. I was halfway through my duties when a wave of intense fear spread over me. My heart pumped with such intensity that I thought it would explode, which intensified the panic that had taken over my mind and body.

I felt the panic of a movie scene where a menacing, lethal demon appeared and I was defenseless prey, fleeing the deadly encounter. I hurried back to my car, stuck the keys in the ignition, and sped home to escape the life-or-death calamity. It was an uncontrollable, irrational, but appropriate response to a nightmare that was undeniably real to me. In my mind, it wasn't a demon that caused a powerful phobic reaction but the supermarket. I found sanctuary in my bedroom, and the anxiety began to lessen, but I felt like I never wanted to leave the protection of those four walls ever again.

I was resigned to the fact I wasn't finishing my sales calls for the day. I tried to make sense of what happened, but it seemed futile, like trying to find meaning in insane thinking. I was emotionally and physically drained and mentally confused. My shirt was drenched in sweat. I stuck my finger between my neck and starched shirt collar, grabbed my necktie, and yanked until both opened from the force, sending the top shirt button across the room. I watched it bounce across the old hardwood floor until it came to a stop, but I continued to stare at it. The panic attack shook me to the core. I felt disconnected from reality, and the episode was so bizarre that I began to second-guess whether it had happened.

The next day, I returned to the supermarket to pick up where I had left off, feeling apprehension the entire ride. I parked my car, took a few steps toward the store, and without warning, fear exploded like a nuclear blast. I felt wave after wave of mushrooming anxiety. Decades of repressed layers of unwanted emotions under a tightly shut lid reached a breaking point and were released like they had a day earlier.

I tried telling my parents about the experience, but they were of a generation that lived through the horrific challenges of World War II and made lives for themselves in the postwar era. They didn't spend time complaining about life; they moved on with it. Here I was describing a psychological nightmare, and their remedy was to put it behind me and move on, but I knew they were concerned.

This was also a time when mental illness carried a stigma and was not openly discussed. Agoraphobia and panic disorder were somewhat unknown. It was before the advent of the internet, so symptoms couldn't be typed into a search engine for instant and spectacular results. At that point, there was no one I knew to turn to for advice.

My Time with Doctors

I felt dizzy and off balance, but I didn't know the source was anxiety. I described the symptoms to my doctor, and he diagnosed an inner ear infection and told me it would heal soon and not to worry. The symptoms continued, and he sent me for a blood test that reported normal overall health.

Next, I was examined by an ear, nose, and throat doctor (ENT) for possible tumors. A brain scan was done, and the results were negative, but my catastrophic thinking continued. I was consumed by doom and ruminated constantly. The ENT physician had said something that seeped into my mind. When he saw the brain scan results were negative and finished his examination, he said that I might want to see a psychologist. I reacted in a polite way to camouflage my disbelief. My thinking was that psychologists were for crazy people, not me. I didn't know of anyone who had visited one. Seeing a psychologist carried a stigma and was a closely guarded secret.

I was in shock about what was happening, confused as to what to do, and doubtful about the ENT doctor's suggestion. I felt I had exhausted all options. An ex-girlfriend's brother had become a psychologist and started a practice nearby. I had always admired him, so I made an appointment. It would turn out to be a decision that helped to get my life back on course though not as I expected.

It wasn't long before he diagnosed me with clinical depression, panic disorder, and agoraphobia. Coming to terms with the diagnosis and the fact that I was oblivious to my true psychological state was a different matter. It would take me nearly three years of determination before I would achieve some normalcy in my life.

My immediate challenge was entering supermarkets, as this was how I made my living. My first panic attack had occurred in a supermarket, and agoraphobia caused me to dread a phobic reaction every time I drove into a supermarket parking lot. Even looking at the building caused a whirlwind of anxiety that spiraled into hyperventilating, dizziness, sweating, and heart palpitations. I was overcome by fear and felt I was the only person on earth who had ever faced these symptoms.

I made five sales calls a day, and in each of the five parking lots I drove to, I had the same reaction. Even the thought of entering a supermarket brought anguish. The first six months of my job were overwhelming, exhausting, and nightmarish. I was so consumed and crippled by the intensity of the experiences that I didn't have the energy or concentration to continue graduate studies, so I made the disheartening decision to skip a semester. My focus was to get through each workday.

The Start of the Calming Method

I had learned a calming method partly from the psychologist. While sitting in my car before entering a supermarket, I would work my way through the sequence of steps. This practice allowed me to understand that my anxiety was never as bad as it felt. I would then enter the supermarket.

Facing the fear of my phobia was probably the most helpful in overcoming it and undeniably the hardest. I practiced the calming method with persistence, determination, and discipline while trying to persevere against the overpowering terror of agoraphobia. In the beginning, I had no faith in the method. I had no practice with it and no reservoir of skill to see positive outcomes. I felt defeated, as the results were miniscule and momentary. As soon as I closed the car door to enter the supermarket, I was hit with a full blast of powerful symptoms.

There is good that can come from adversity, though it may not be evident as we make our way through it. The one thing I developed as a young boy, living under a tightfisted upbringing, was an unshakable resolve to defy failure, an attribute that came to define my life. I relied on determination to help me navigate and achieve results in sports, business, politics, raising a family, hobbies, and achieving other aspirations in my life, whether big or small.

At that point, I used it to embark on my toughest test: working through agoraphobia and managing panic attacks.

After six months, I still didn't understand what I was going through, even though I was meeting with a psychologist every other week. I used the calming method for panic attacks and was able to get through each workday, but at day's end, I was overwhelmed and exhausted. It felt as if I had lived my life in the wide-open space of rural America with its slow pace and folksy charm and, without warning, was dropped into the middle of the metropolitan mayhem that was New York City. I was confused and navigating my way by relying on instinct, but at that point, I felt capable of returning to graduate school and enrolled for the next semester.

Approaching a supermarket entrance was becoming more tolerable, but I still had to use the calming method with diligence, so I practiced it in the car. I'd enter the store and quickly attack each responsibility, make sure that the product was displayed properly on shelves, check inventory, write credits for spoilage, hand my report to the department manager, and leave.

I was able to complete each task without interruption but without much more than a polite hello to employees, and then I would escape the confines of the store. If the manager stopped me to discuss something, I felt cornered. I'd answer questions without pleasantries so I could minimize the conversation and leave. I wasn't making tremendous psychological progress toward overcoming agoraphobia or panic disorder, but blind determination had me performing the basics of my job so I could earn a living. My calm façade masked the inner chaos.

This was a period when I was driven by my refusal to accept a lifetime of mental limitations, so even slow progress made me more defiant and determined. Fortunately, working as a sales representative allowed me freedom from managerial oversight, so no one was present to see how crippled I was at performing my job. If my boss went into a store to see if I was properly doing my assignments, the evidence was made obvious by fully stocked shelves and a confirmation by a department manager.

I had been dating Carol for about one year. An hour drive separated our homes, and since we both had full-time jobs and I had graduate school most evenings, I saw her on Wednesday and Saturday nights. She was aware of my anxiety but not to the full extent because she didn't see me often enough to witness it, and I was able to conceal much of it. I wasn't being purposely deceitful; I just didn't understand much of what I was going through and had a singular focus to overcome it.

I saw her more during the summers because she visited my shore house on weekends, and the improvements in coping with agoraphobia and panic disorder, along with our developing relationship, were fatefully synchronized. I was able to see that her nature, values, and overall outlook on life were remarkably similar to mine, and I knew this was a good foundation for a lifelong relationship. I was also impressed with her commitment to stay with me, knowing I was going through a challenging time.

There is no question this was a dark period for me, and Carol was a ray of light. A year after my initial mental health crisis, I could see I was making progress, but it would take more time before I could manage my anxiety. Repeatedly facing my fear was loosening the grip that phobic reactions had over me but not completely ending them. I felt the efforts were rewiring my brain; it was functioning differently than it had previously, and I was more comfortable around people at my job and in graduate school.

It reminded me of the process that occurs when learning to play a musical instrument. At first, coordinating the hands to play the correct notes and in the right tempo is awkward and seems impossible, but when repeated over and over, it becomes second nature.

There was also a growing understanding that when I threw myself into the phobic fire, I exited unscorched. I was getting more comfortable dealing with the mental and physical turmoil, but some remained.

Georgia's Not on My Mind

I consider this period the "crawling phase" of developing coping skills, but crawling wasn't fast enough for the pace of life, and life chose to ramp up the speed. I received a call from my boss, telling me about a national sales meeting that I needed to attend in Atlanta, Georgia. I would need to fly from New Jersey to Atlanta in the confined space of a long, narrow fuselage for nearly two hours without any means of escape.

Instantaneously, my mind retraced the last flight I had taken years earlier when I sat in a plane and was stuck on the tarmac for two hours. My mind raced with worry. I felt trapped by the prospect of boarding the plane. I felt trapped at having to be away from home for five days. I felt trapped at being forced to interact with coworkers for extended periods, stuck in meetings and having to socialize at night.

I compared the anxiety to what I felt when I had lived on the college campus and the panicked thoughts that I would have to remain over a weekend, but then, I was able to dodge my fears by driving home. Confronting my fear of going into supermarkets was one thing, because I could escape through the exit doors if necessary, but a stay in Atlanta offered no immediate getaway. The decision was mostly out of my control, or at least I felt it was, since quitting my job wasn't an option. This aspect fueled enormous anxiety for the weeks leading up to the meeting. I felt alone, desperate, depressed, and worried. Every time I thought about it, I felt worse, but having spent a year facing my anxieties provided some confidence, trembling as it was, to go on the trip.

I was able to manage my overwhelming feelings during my stay. I wouldn't say I coped with them ideally, certainly not in any productive way. I spent most of my time watching the clock and convincing myself I could endure the mental mayhem until the meeting ended and I got home. The night before the meeting ended, I finally experienced a sense of relief. I was going home soon, and my anxiety was lessening. Even my sense of humor returned, which was always a sign that I was feeling good. I had endured the challenge, not that I would want to do it again.

At 6:00 p.m., I received a message that my boss wanted to see me, I wasn't given a reason. I went to his hotel room and noticed that three salespeople had arrived before me. Since they all loved to play cards, I figured I was summoned to join them in a game of poker.

He wasn't a bad boss, and he gave me leeway when it came to running my sales territory. Even though he didn't know about my anxiety, the freedom he allowed me was helpful to my recovery, but he had the impatience of a salesperson. He reminded me of someone peddling so fast that they failed to notice they didn't own a bike. As with most bosses, he was looking to make a name for himself and didn't mind being a guy who flattered and agreed with his boss to make himself look good, regardless of merit. It was his way of gaining an advantage in the pursuit of his career.

That day, he had a job to do to make his boss happy. He was told to choose four guys to drive a company car in the parking lot to New Jersey, and I had been volunteered. It was the reason I was summoned to his hotel room. My heart sank. The finish line of my five-day anxiety marathon was being moved further away by two days. My mind was preoccupied with the fact that I would be forced to engage with three guys for two days. I'd have to disguise my panic while confined in a car, nose distance from each of them. I was devastated and didn't know if I had the resolve to get through the task.

The next morning, as the four of us piled into the sedan and started our journey, I resigned myself to the situation and began to feel I could do it. I was *willing* to live the situation. Once again, I was being forced to face my anxieties instead of running from them, and it was a major step in learning to cope, which ultimately helped in my recovery.

After a few hours, I was enjoying myself. I was still clinically depressed, but I was with a bunch of guys in their twenties, finding ways to laugh. One of the guys was goofy, telling us about the funny mistakes he was making on sales calls. Another guy was witty and quick with riotous jokes, and the other was self-deprecating, making us laugh by making himself look bad.

The two days I spent with the guys affirmed that the calming method I had learned was helpful, because I used it a few times. It also demonstrated that I'd made considerable progress by throwing myself into the fires of anxiety. Determination to do it was driving progress. I began to see the possibility of freeing myself from the limitations imposed by depression, agoraphobia, and panic disorder to live a life of my choosing or at least close enough to be satisfied with it.

I continued to make progress during the year that followed. My anxiety was diminishing, and I was comfortably overseeing my work and personal responsibilities. I was ready to move to the next step of building a career and was seeking a sales management position.

I had outgrown the cramped living quarters I shared with my good friend. Our relationship became strained, and we agreed to sell the property and go our separate ways.

I was in my last semester of graduate school, and my relationship with Carol was well into its third year. I had just turned thirty. Our time together had proven that our relationship had a solid foundation for building a life together. Her ability to deal with my idiosyncrasies had been an invaluable proving ground. I was advancing my career, our relationship was healthy, and we were practically finishing each other's sentences. I asked her to marry me, and we stood next to each other at the altar seven months later.

Getting Better All the Time

About a year after our wedding, Carol was pregnant, and we moved from our one-bedroom condo into a new home. Our son, Anthony Jr., was born five months later in January 1988. Our daughter, Tori, was born in March 1990. During this time, I was working as a sales manager at a New Jersey facility for a national distributor of medical supplies. Being a sales manager and managing people was my goal when

I enrolled in graduate school. I was ecstatic that it was now realized, especially in view of the major setbacks and uncertainties of the preceding years.

My anxiety wasn't gone, but it wasn't the central influence on how I lived like it had been. I was coping with fear, managing it and getting beyond flare-ups before they became full-blown attacks, but an undercurrent of anxiety was always present. I was always on edge. If I was sleeping and Carol startled me, I shot up in bed with a raised fist as if someone had broken into our home and was threatening us. I never took a swing at her, as I'd quickly come to my senses, realizing that there was no threat.

I loved family life. It was important for me that our children knew how deeply they were loved. Carol and I smothered them with affection, and they saw the same love between their parents. I coached some of their sports teams, helped them with homework, went to all their school events, and roughhoused with them. On Saturday mornings, I put on music, and we'd dance around the house. Carol and I were as involved as any parents could be in their children's lives.

It had been five years since I had my first mental health crisis and was diagnosed with depression, panic disorder, and agoraphobia. Since then, I was promoted from sales manager to general manager of the New Jersey distribution facility, and two years later, I was given the added responsibility of the Connecticut facility. I was responsible for the sales and operations of $60 million dollars and eighty employees. I spent a week at each location, but I didn't like being away from the family.

The company had a national sales meeting each year, and an upcoming one was scheduled in Texas. I had a sinus infection and my energy was depleted. I had asked my boss if I could skip the event and use the time for recovery, but he felt my absence would be a poor reflection on him, so he insisted that I attend.

My sinuses were swollen and blocked, which affected the pressure on my eardrum. As the plane descended at Dallas/Fort Worth International Airport, I was daydreaming and looking through the window when I was startled by a pain in my ear as if a pencil was stabbed into it. Apparently, it was caused by an imbalance between the pressure in my ear and that of the plane. I felt miserable and, for some reason, considerable stress.

The first order of business for all the managers was lunch. I entered an enormous room with large circular tables, each with ten chairs. The company had just reached $1 billion dollars in sales, and it was putting on an impressive display in commemoration. Most of the seating was filled, and the one spot I saw open was next to an executive vice president and officer of the company. He was a hefty guy—two seats could be used to fully accommodate his generous size—and he didn't have the jolly disposition associated with such a short, plump, round fellow. He had an extremely high profile in the company, and any aspiring businessperson would jump at the opportunity to network with him, but I was feeling so ill that he was the last person I wanted seated next to me. I felt trapped.

As I brought the first forkful of salad from the plate to my mouth, I was overcome by panic. My face flushed, and I felt sweat forming on my forehead. During this moment, the VP turned to say hello. The obligation of my polite response was hanging in the air as catastrophic thoughts raced through my mind and I felt an impending panic attack. I wanted to bolt and run for the exit, but my experi-

Anthony P. Mauro Sr.

ence with panic attacks and using the calming method was second nature, so I turned to him and responded warmly, "Hello." The feelings of doom and the need to escape slowly dissolved as we engaged in conversation. I was able to make it through the balance of the sales meeting without any issues.

The fact remained that I had to cope with anxiety. It didn't matter that the panic attacks were manageable. The experience I had with the VP was disappointing—it was a frustration, a vulnerability that I wanted to make disappear, and my determination to make it happen was as strong as ever. Coping with anxiety and managing panic attacks wasn't enough. I wanted them gone from my life.

Mysticism

When I was in my early twenties, I was fascinated by Hinduism and its doctrines of the continuous cycle of life, death, and reincarnation as well as the universal law of cause and effect. Hindus believe that living creatures have a soul that is part of the supreme soul, and the goal is to achieve salvation. Salvation ends the cycles of rebirths. A fundamental principle of this religion is that thoughts and actions determine current life and future lives. There is equanimity for those of higher consciousness.

Having been raised Catholic, Hinduism was such a departure from church teachings that I found it interesting, and I also saw there was a parallel to science. I had read about the law of conservation of energy in a basic science class in high school. It stated that energy could neither be created nor destroyed, only transferred from one form to another. I remembered the example provided was a stick of dynamite exploding, and the chemical energy contained within the dynamite changed into kinetic energy, heat, and light. The point was that when all the energy was added together, it equaled the starting chemical energy value.

I saw a similarity between the law of conservation of energy and religious beliefs in an afterlife. My thinking was that "consciousness" was energy; it survived the death of the physical body and wasn't destroyed. This idea helped widen my perspective, to see there was a greater purpose to living and that life was largely beyond my control. Since events outside my control were a source of anxiety, Hinduism became more than a curiosity.

Another correlation with science I found intriguing was between karma and Newton's third law of motion that "to every action, there is an equal and opposite reaction." Karma is a spiritual cause and effect; all our thoughts, words, and actions begin a chain of reactions, and we personally experience the effects of everything we cause. With these parallels to science, Hinduism expanded my understanding that life was bigger than my anxieties and that healing might be found outside the model of psychological therapy and traditional medicine.

Though Hinduism and The Sedona Method didn't seem to be the solutions I was searching for, they made me mindful of the basic cause of my anxiety: wanting to control the uncontrollable. They also made me conscious of the futility of such an exercise. This awareness was sowing a seed that I didn't begin to water until four decades later due to Carol's FTD.

Back to Work

A few years had passed since the panic attack at the sales meeting in Texas. I eventually left the company for an opportunity to start an institutional pharmacy, a company that distributed medicines to people in nursing homes. Starting and building a company had been one of my goals when I enrolled in graduate school. Finally, I was firing on all cylinders personally and professionally.

It wasn't until I was forty years old that the next panic disorder episode affected my life. I had taken a job as the senior vice president for a company in New York City and commuted by bus. After one month, I started to feel stress, but I thought it was job related. I had difficulty concentrating, I was losing weight, my energy was low, and I was irritable. The symptoms were like the hum of background noise, and I wasn't completely aware of them.

One day in late August, as I commuted home, the air was heavy with humidity, and the woman seated next to me was devotedly self-absorbed. She spoke any thought that burst into her mind; there were many. She was oblivious to the imbalance between her talking and me listening, which became advantageous because she was so focused on herself that she couldn't see my preoccupation was using the calming method to manage the terror of a panic attack.

Because of traffic congestion, it took three hours to travel what was normally a one-hour ride, and when I finally arrived at the commuter parking lot, I was greeted by an empty spot that had formerly been home to my car.

I tell people not to sweat the small stuff, and they might as well not sweat the big stuff either, since it's just a bigger version of the small stuff. I was taking my own advice during the next hour as I found myself helping a police officer file a stolen car report. I walked home. I was physically and mentally exhausted from the day's events and all that had led up to it. I needed time to mend.

I left the company. Carol and our children depended on me to provide for them, and we had enough money saved to get us through the next several months. I wasn't sure about my next step, but my history of coping with depression, agoraphobia, and panic disorder, and my determination to not have my condition define or limit me, gave me a sense that things would work out. Into each life some rain must fall, and to heal was to learn to dance in it.

Contrary to the doomsday thinking that came with panic disorder and depression, I'd always had an intrinsic sense of optimism about life—a naïve confidence that things would work out even when there wasn't evidence to support it. I knew my thoughts could be clouds that hid the sun. Another quirk of mine was to never curse the heavens over my ailment. If anything, I prayed for help in finding a way through my situation. I knew that some people suffered far worse than me.

As timing would have it, my father-in-law had started a home-based brokerage business in the manufacturing services industry and suggested for years that I do the same. I never considered his suggestion because I wanted to establish myself in the larger business arena, but I realized that I had accomplished my goals of managing a midsized business and starting one from scratch. Apparently, I had stored his suggestion somewhere in my mind. In this moment of job uncertainty, I saw an opportunity to start a brokerage business. Launching and running a business was a deeply ingrained skill; it was second nature. Even though I knew nothing about the manufacturing services industry, I knew the formula for creating and managing any business was essentially the same. The only difference was understanding the features and benefits of

Anthony P. Mauro Sr.

the products or services being sold. At forty years old, I started a similar business, and as of this writing, nearly three decades later, I still enjoy doing it. Since it's a home-based company, a major benefit is being able to enjoy my family. I was present every day to raise our kids with Carol and savor a full family life.

I was also able to pursue various hobbies, one of which was starting a New Jersey environmental organization that educated legislators about conservation of natural resources. I used my business experience to establish it, and it was soon recognized as a top lobbying group in the state government. It was comprised of a charity, a political action committee, and a nonprofit membership organization. This is stated not for pomposity but to publicize that a person can live a gratifying life despite being inclined to mental disorders, maybe even thrive because of them.

During a ten-year stretch, I traveled to remote areas of Zimbabwe, Canada, South Africa, New Zealand, the Alaskan mainland, Kodiak Island, and much of the United States without issue. I walked flatlands and climbed mountains. It was a long way from the days of fleeing my college campus on weekends to avoid intense anxiety.

A Little Adventure

I had one more panic attack during this period, and it happened on a wilderness trip in the mountains of New Zealand.

Working as a guide is a mentally and physically demanding profession and comes with being tired and hungry. They get up before light and get to bed late. They work in heat, rain, wind, sleet, or snow. It is a labor of love. They have to be patient, respectful, ethical, and persistent in practicing their trade and ensuring client safety.

I met my guide at the airport. I don't remember his name, but I remember he was intense and straightforward. He was a practical man, the type who didn't understand how an airline could be overbooked or why a restaurant did not have a seat ready when arriving on time for a reservation. He had a lot of confidence in himself, and it made me overlook his small stature. His greeting was a grunt with an outstretched hand, and his hand was as hard and dried as tough leather. I imagined it was scarred and bruised due to his trade.

We drove along a ten-mile stretch of riverbed to the base of a mountain that was part of the Southern Alps, a mountain range extending along much of New Zealand's South Island. It was here that we would begin our climb the next day. We set up a tent designed for two people, and it was very tight quarters. We intended to break camp early the next morning.

About 9:00 p.m., a pelting rain began. I turned on my flashlight and saw the tent's flexible support poles shuddering from gale-force winds. The downpour was relentless for twenty-four hours and then turned into a severe blizzard. We didn't leave our tiny confines for thirty-six hours, and when we did, we stood in snow that was thigh high. We spent nine hours trying to move our vehicle, but the wheels spun uselessly, and the snow was too deep to navigate. By day's end, we had progressed a mere two hundred yards from where we had set up the tent. We gave up when the truck's front axle became lodged on a large rock hidden under a snowdrift.

Though I had been trapped in the tent during the storm, I didn't experience anxiety. In fact, I was enjoying the adventure, but when we took a break from trying to move

Anthony P. Mauro Sr.

the truck, I must have realized I was trapped in the wilderness and was overcome by a wave of panic. I was talking to my guide as the panic attack happened, and my thoughts raced through catastrophic scenarios and fear of embarrassment. Just as unexpectedly, a composure came over me. I thought, *I've been here before. I've got this handled.* The attack dissolved as quickly as it had appeared. I'd gotten so used to working my way through panic attacks with the calming method that I didn't need to rely on it. My guide was never the wiser.

In the end, we were able to radio a helicopter to rescue us. We later learned that the blizzard was one of the worst New Zealand had experienced in decades.

Over years of using the calming method for managing panic attacks, I didn't realize that facing up to anxiety was the key to starving it of attention. My brain was being rewired to function differently from how it had previously, a phenomenon known as neuroplasticity. The experience of overcoming fear and anxiety, as difficult as it was, helped to provide the confidence that I'd get through the panic attacks, and this eventually allowed me to do many of the things I wanted to do in life. I was starting to understand that of all the serious considerations that face us during our lifetime, perhaps the most serious is not to take life too seriously.

Though I was able to manage the panic attacks, I wasn't completely free of them. Carol's FTD, my grief, and life changes on the horizon would test this ability and help me get to the root of my anxiety.

NOVEMBER 2018

Back to Carol

I was sitting in front of Carol as she sat in a chair similar to one found in a dentist's office. Two months had passed since her official diagnosis of FTD, and she was about to receive her first TMS treatment. The medical equipment was next to her on a cart. A device that had a magnetic coil inside a housing was positioned on her head using landmarks Dr. Devi put on her scalp. The coil was connected to a pulse stimulator.

It was a relatively new way to use magnetism to stimulate nerve cells. It did not require surgery but transmitted magnetic pulses through the brain by pressing a housing against the skull. When stimulation was applied, there was a series of rapid clicking sounds. Carol never flinched, complained, or said anything negative when the stimulation was applied, so I assumed it was a comfortable procedure.

Dr. Devi was clear that there was no therapy to cure FTD but that TMS had therapeutic potential, so I agreed it was in the best interest of Carol's health. The TMS regimen required weekly visits to New York City from our home in central New Jersey. The first few years, we traveled by train since this avoided the city's gridlock traffic. We took the 9:32 a.m. North Jersey Coast Line from Aberdeen and arrived at New York Penn Station at 10:41 a.m.

Carol's obsessive thinking was becoming more pronounced, and she was still compelled to say the name of each approaching station stop and do the same on the return home.

I'd hail a cab, and we'd ride from New York Penn Station to the doctor's office on Seventy-Sixth Street, traveling about fifty city blocks. After a few weeks, we opted for the subway, so we walked to Herald Square, rode to Seventy-Second Street, and walked the remaining blocks.

Carol still had a good sense of direction at that point. She could direct me to the subway stop and navigate our walk to the doctor's office, but I knew it was from memory, and if I changed the route by substituting one street or avenue for another, she would get confused. This was unsettling, as I realized that if we ever became separated or something happened to me, she would be overwhelmed and lost in one of the largest cities in the world.

I put the Find My app on our cell phones. I found it easy to use for real-time location sharing and tracking. Our son and daughter also put it on their cell phones so that multiple people could monitor Carol's location. Since Carol was prone to fiddling with her phone, misplacing it, or mistakenly deleting apps, I eventually bought an Apple watch and put it in her pocket so she wouldn't misplace it and I could track her if necessary.

The Handsomest Man in the Room

As Carol was receiving her TMS treatment, I thought of some of the early FTD symptoms I hadn't recognized. I remembered being at a friend's party in May 2017 and noticing that Carol had gained weight. I wasn't focused on her weight but was surprised because she meticulously watched her diet and kept herself thin and fit for our entire marriage. Even after giving birth to two children, she maintained a weight of 115 lbs., so gaining twenty pounds was unlike her.

The other thing I recalled was being at a dinner party and sitting at a large table along with others and chatting idly. Carol turned to me and said I was the handsomest man in the room within earshot of the people next to us. We were affectionate and complimentary of each other throughout our marriage, but I had never heard her flatter me in such a sweet way, and her shy nature would not have had her say it in front of others. It was so genuine a moment that I am touched by it to this day.

As Carol's TMS treatment ended, I questioned why I was trying to identify the first signs of FTD. Maybe I was grieving or sensed that years of incremental loss remained. Maybe I was already witnessing the pattern of slow psychological and physical decline. I could see changes in her mannerisms, her lost ability to follow recipes for the foods she loved to cook, and her compromised decision making.

Thinking of these losses created angst as I tried to understand what was happening to her and cope with the slow, dramatic changes. I was losing her companionship, her sense of humor, her problem-solving abilities, the intimacy of our relationship, and the deepness of our connection. She was slowly disappearing before my eyes, like a puzzle losing one piece at a time, and we couldn't say goodbye to each other in any practical way. I didn't know how to process the sense of loss or recognize my grief since she was still in my life. I knew the disease would worsen but couldn't predict when or how or the ever-increasing need for care.

My friends and family were well meaning but couldn't understand the vague sorrow associated with FTD. They tried to be positive by saying Carol was still alive and that I had time to spend with her, but the words were awkward and missed the subtleties of the loss. This amplified my loneliness.

Ahead of me were years of processing grief, but at the moment, I was stunned, exhausted, anxious, and fearful that my own history of mental illness would cripple me from managing my responsibilities. The idea wasn't acceptable, and thinking about the possibility added more stress.

Really, More Adversity?

It was an autumn day, and I was enjoying the scenery from our deck in the backyard. The air was brisk. The leaves shivered from the wind, and some took the moment to acknowledge mortality and let go of their host branch, then gracefully swirl to the earth below. I could almost smell winter nearing.

I walked inside and hung my jacket on the hook next to the door. Carol was watching TV a few feet away, and I joined her on the couch. Our two dogs were relaxed and comfortable, like dogs get when they completely trust their surroundings.

My cell phone rang, and I saw on the screen that it was Tori. I answered and could tell by her voice that something was wrong; experience made me an expert in knowing how she segued into shocking news. She wasted no time admitting that she had now relapsed on oxycodone. Her revelation was devastating news, as our efforts to help her through recovery years earlier had taken a toll on our family. Carol and I understood addiction could be chronic and relapses were a possibility, so I was proud of Tori's admission and that she was asking for my help. Although she had only been taking oxycodone for one week, she realized she was in over her head. Successful recovery required honesty, and honesty was challenging.

I was sure being open about it lifted a heavy burden from her, and it deepened our connection. Neither Tori nor I thought relapse was a failure but rather that recovery was an achievement. As I have emphasized to my kids throughout their lives, I don't focus on how people fall but pay attention to how they rise. Tori had proven herself in this regard. Embracing life's changeability had taught her that difficulties could be overcome and that life was full of possibilities.

She wanted to give herself a fresh start with detox treatment and wanted me to help her and her new husband, Andrew, navigate the "where, when, and how much" aspects. I was glad to help.

Tori was on the speaker phone when she made her admission about relapsing. Carol was sitting next to me, so she overheard the conversation and witnessed my profound concern.

As the call ended, I momentarily uttered my disbelief and turned to Carol, thinking I would hear the same. Instead, she was relaxed and composed. She asked me, "Is there anything good on Netflix?" I saw her indifference as a sign of FTD. It was the opposite of how she had overseen Tori's first fight with addiction.

The Long Arm of Addiction

To have a child addicted to a drug is a tragic reality for any parent, and the first addiction episode devastated our family. Carol had uncovered Tori's oxycodone usage and was relentless in trying to intervene to the point of mental and physical exhaustion.

The impact of addiction on the brain is complex and can debilitate a person until they become unrecognizable. With continued use of opioids, their ability to think rationally and make sound decisions breaks down. Carol went to great lengths to stop Tori from using the drug and meticulously unraveled her deceitfulness, and though it was an impossible endeavor, Carol was consumed by it. I had respect for her instincts and assertiveness.

Our marriage was no different than most in that our roles complemented one another, one incomplete without the other. During the first addiction episode, Carol led the charge in surveilling and managing Tori while I focused on a solution to the nightmare. I was frantically absorbed in trying to understand addiction and find a means for recovery. I called several doctors and treatment centers, and they all recommended Suboxone, an opioid addiction replacement. Though Suboxone had plenty of success stories, it also had the potential for abuse and addiction, since it was itself an opioid.

Some doctors believed this was replacing one addiction for another. Regardless of the merits, Suboxone wasn't the therapy I thought was best for Tori, even though it was the standard FDA-approved medication for treating opioid use and withdrawal.

I hit a dead end and wasn't sure where to turn when I learned of a doctor who used a different approach. He used an injectable version of Vivitrol (Naltrexone), a prescription medicine used to prevent opioid dependence relapses after detoxification. The medicine blocked the opioid from binding to receptors in the brain, which diminished cravings and the euphoric effect. It was not addictive and had no potential for abuse. Naltrexone had been used to treat alcohol abuse, but it was proving successful in treating opioid addiction.

The first thing I needed to do was have Tori agree to a thirty-day stay in a treatment center. Treatment with Vivitrol could only be administered fourteen days after the last opioid use. The thirty days provided an intensive, focused environment including therapy, education, relapse prevention training, and more. Tori decided to get help at a center two hours from our home. I made the arrangements for the following day.

In the morning, as Carol and I got in the car with Tori, she changed her mind and bolted for freedom up our driveway. I acted out of instinct, chased after her, and escorted her back to the car. I could see that Tori wanted to stop but that it took more than good intentions and strong will. It was hard for the rest of us to witness a drug so powerful that it made our daughter unrecognizable. There is torment in being addicted.

After one week, Carol received a call from the rehab center to report that Tori was leaving the program early. Since there was nothing they could legally do to prevent her from leaving, Carol asked me to speak with her. I called Tori, and she insisted that I pick her up. I knew that agreeing with her would mean she couldn't start the treatment with Vivitrol since it was too soon and would cause immediate withdrawal. I also knew that for her to leave early was a mistake. Any work to that point would be wasted, since treatment was a process that needed completion to get the most from it.

Tori threatened that if we didn't come get her, she would walk to a nearby city and find a way home herself. I knew city temptations would be powerful and that she wasn't into her treatment long enough to have a chance at avoiding relapse. I also knew that the stress her addiction placed on all of us was unbearable and was concerned about how the fabric of our family would be torn. An impossibly difficult decision was forced on me, one almost as torturous and inconceivable as the one in the movie *Sophie's Choice*, where a mother must choose which of her children will be spared death. I faced giving my twenty-three-year-old daughter an ultimatum: one choice would help her health and the mental health of our family, and the other was potentially losing her to the horrors of addiction and the menaces of city street life. I told Tori that if she left the center early, she would not have a home to return to until she had recovered.

I ended the call. The thought of never seeing her again was unimaginable.

Carol agreed that the decision was in everyone's best interest and that Tori would truly suffer if we caved to her demands. As convinced as we were with our reasoning, my heart sank into my stomach, and my mind ruminated on "what ifs." I knew Carol's demeanor well enough to see her fear and anxiety. We spent the night tossing and turning in bed and didn't speak of the phone conversation.

Parents invest every fiber of themselves raising their children; we nurse them back to health, watch over them as they sleep, love them when they aren't loveable, and do everything in our power to protect and guide them through life. They are a symbol of the future, and losing them to drugs or death is a loss of hopes and dreams. It is inconceivable heartbreak.

The next day, I got out of bed early. It was unusually quiet, and my crippling sense of concern was so pervasive that I wondered if it was the reason the birds weren't singing. I had my coffee and wasn't sure what to do with myself since it would be hours before I could call the treatment center, so I had a second cup. Adrenaline was already coursing through me, and combined with the effects of the coffee, I was shaky. I exercised for forty-five minutes, which was my daily routine, and started to feel some composure.

As soon as my digital watch read 8:00, the hour the rehab center opened, I tapped the facility's number on my cell phone. I was on hold for several minutes. Some people say that listening to music while on hold makes their wait feel shorter, but I am not among them. A male counselor came on the line. I could tell he was a young man by his clear, light, pleasant voice, which added sweetness to his report that Tori had decided to stay until the end of her treatment. Carol and I were overcome with relief.

We picked Tori up at the end of her stay and took her directly to the doctor who used the injectable Vivitrol therapy. It turned out that the treatment was an excellent choice.

Back to Tori's Relapse Phone Call

I was sitting next to Carol on the couch in our home as Tori announced her relapse over my cell phone speaker. After years of Vivitrol treatments, Tori had stopped months earlier.

When Carol overheard Tori telling me she had relapsed, she knew the stress-filled and painful history of the first episode. This made Carol's response to the news of the relapse, "Is there anything good on Netflix?" a poignant moment in understanding the degree of Carol's FTD degeneration that had occurred since her symptoms appeared five years earlier. It was another harsh reminder that I was losing my wife's companionship, our ability to experience life together, our connection, and our shared reality. Again, I felt deep sorrow in knowing that they could never be retrieved. This is a recurring experience as I deal with FTD.

I was confronted with helping Tori's husband of two months, Andrew, to navigate choosing another treatment and detoxification facility, investigate whether there was medical coverage, and provide emotional support with her recovery. It was a big task for a twenty-eight-year-old new-lywed, but we made our way through it. Fortunately, Tori's recognition of her problem was so soon that she needed only two weeks to detox and was progressively reintroduced to the Vivitrol and therapy regimen that had worked previously. She has been well ever since and is raising a daughter with Andrew.

The stress of her relapse couldn't have come at a worse time since I was also caring and grieving for Carol. I was still trying to make sense of my upended life. The major changes taking place shook my world, but the pressure was forcing me to interact with life in a new way, a larger way. I was adapting to the new demands out of necessity.

I was still coping with anxiety but relieved that I hadn't suffered a major panic attack or lapsed into depression or agoraphobia. I was helping lead the people I loved through a difficult period in their lives while meeting the demands of caring for my wife, but I was not living, just existing. I was making automatic decisions that didn't line up with how I wanted to live, disengaged from my routines and going through the motions of getting through each day. I continued going to the gym and maintaining my routines, but doing them felt as if I was dragging dead elephants behind me. Every ache was magnified. Friends complimented me on how well I was managing everything, and I suppose on the outside it that appeared I was, but their words were foreign to me.

Tori began talking with a therapist to learn how to cope with her mother's dementia and also became involved in an FTD support group to learn how others with loved ones having FTD were handling their circumstances. It was a healthy sign that her coping skills were improving, and I fully supported her efforts. She worked for me in my home-based business, and we talked about her concerns often. Since she was in our house five days a week, it was especially painful for her to watch her mother worsen as the years went by.

Anthony Jr. and I started to spend time together every Saturday, going to microbreweries. Beer tasting had become his hobby, and I did it for enjoyment and for his company. He was coping with his mother's FTD differently than Tori. We talked about FTD but not as frequently as I did with Tori, and his outlook was that talking about it changed nothing and only made him sad. His exposure to Carol was less than Tori's—he saw his mom once per week, and this allowed him to process his mom's disease differently, since he didn't witness it daily.

My approach was to keep them grounded, remind them there was every reason to be optimistic regarding their health, discuss new research and developments, and provide them with available resources. The truth was that coping with FTD was confusing and overwhelming for all of us.

They saw their mother's abilities degenerating and understood that more upsetting changes would come. I remained available, flexible, and candid with them, because ignorance breeds fear and fantasies, which can have a worse impact than reality.

As for me, I had a history of relying on myself instead of others for answers and personal direction. It was not that I didn't seek or value opinions from friends and professionals. I was open minded in that regard, but I'd been self-reliant most of my life and needed to find answers and direction from within myself. I worked hard to be honest with myself. A person who avoids being honest with himself avoids the clarity needed to make wise decisions.

THE YEAR 2019

Something Different

Six months passed with weekly visits to Dr. Devi. In February of 2019, Carol and I were on the train to New York City for one of our regular visits. The route and Carol's rituals were ordinary, but I always managed to find something fascinating in life if I took the time to search it out, and this was one of those days.

I hailed a cab a few blocks from Penn Station, and the driver was more receptive to conversation than most, which I'm sure he regretted after my thirty-minute, non-stop investigation into his life. I'd always wondered what attracted people to their professions. Given that this fellow was politely receptive, he became a victim of my enthusiasm, and I peppered him with questions.

This cabbie, Tom, was clean shaven, including his head. A dimpled smile added warmth to his face, but a pensive brow and no-nonsense demeanor subtracted from it. His jawline was as angled as a steel box. He was not the typical-looking New York City cabbie, which was a temptation to my curious nature. He was an extravagant talker, in his early sixties, and newly retired, ending his career as a three-star general after four decades of service to the army. He had been involved in missions that were too secretive to divulge. Driving a cab was on his bucket list. His father drove a cab his entire adult life and had reminded Tom that military service was not a "real job." He had criticized him for being able to avoid working a real job his entire life.

Although his father had passed away, Tom felt obligated to honor him by working as a New York City cabbie for one month and would then move on to the next item on his bucket list. I don't recall what the next item was, but I remember he said he would do it in Arizona.

Tom was a good match for my questions, and the more I asked, the more he answered. He told me about taxi driving and passengers. He said that if there was a sign of trouble, he could push a panic button underneath the dash to summon the nearest city police cruiser. It activated amber lights in the front and rear of the taxi. He had never had to use it.

He told me that waving your arms like an eager kid knowing the answer to a teacher's question wasn't the best way to get a cabbie's attention. The correct method was to step a bit, but not too far, into the street and wave an arm to catch the driver's eye. At that point, you made eye contact to signal to the driver that you were trying to get his attention and not that of your spouse across the street. Tom said you could even hail with your nose if your arms were full of a day's worth of shopping items. I imagined that a generous nose would garner better results.

If for some reason you want to endear yourself to a taxi driver, in addition to a lavish gratuity, you should avoid being rude by closing the partition separating the front and back seats, not ask them to run red lights or make illegal turns, and not suggest they drive safely, since all sane cabbies start the day with that in mind.

I learned that Tom liked it when people turned off the taxi TV, since it was a loop he listened to all day, every day.

Let's Get Outta Here

We arrived for our noon appointment with a few minutes to spare. I always began the visit with Dr. Devi by going over any changes I had seen with Carol since our last visit. Her TMS treatments, done by assistants, were weekly, but we were now meeting with Dr. Devi every other month. I asked her if I could take Carol on vacation, and she loved the idea.

A few months later, I was sitting next to Carol on a flight to Arizona to escape the stresses of daily life for a week. She was pressing buttons on the seatback screen; I helped her find a movie, and this seemed to satisfy her restlessness. The woman in front of me reclined her seat as if she were launching a military attack, startling me as it slammed into my knees. Leg room is always problematic for me on flights since my legs are long, and I try to be on alert for such collisions, but my attention had wandered.

I had asked Carol if she'd like to take a vacation since we hadn't been on one in years. We had been saving money so that we could see the world when we retired, which I thought would be in two years, but as the adage goes, "Man plans, and God laughs."

Our vacation destination was Sedona, Arizona. I liked the idea because Sedona was known as a spiritual mecca for rejuvenation and chasing a higher purpose. It was marketed as having energy vortexes that filled people with a desire to nourish their souls and transform their lives. I wasn't sure if this was a pitch from inventive ad agency minds or the gospel truth, but I hadn't shaken the sense that I had to eliminate my anxiety and try to raise my consciousness.

My ambitions made Sedona ideal for me, and Carol was thrilled by the prospect of walking among ancient red rocks, crystal streams, and desert landscapes, witnessing nature's beauty. She seemed most excited about the fact that I agreed to rent a convertible for our seven-day stay and had booked a helicopter tour of the Grand Canyon. She brought it up to our kids at every opportunity and to every passerby who paused long enough for her to blurt it out. I was happy to see her happy.

Our flight from New Jersey landed at Phoenix Airport in Arizona. We then rented a car and drove two hours through a drastically changing desert landscape to arrive at our hotel in Sedona. The city is part of the Colorado Plateau. It has a desert climate with sunny weather most of the year. All the red rock formations are formed by erosion. There are no actual mountains. The resort was situated on the banks of Oak Creek with exceptional views.

From our hotel room window, we could see the portrait-like rock formations and beautifully landscaped gardens. Works of art by local artists were exhibited throughout the hotel. As far as I was concerned, we were staying in a modern-day sanctuary. At night, we sat in the courtyard and looked up at the vivid stars. They looked like they were hand-tossed diamonds against a black velvet backdrop. Carol told me she loved the view, so we sat outside every night. Both the stars and her presence were comforting— signs of hope, though I understood that hope was possible only with intervention by the divine and not modern medi- cine. Strangely, the night sky also reminded me of our fleeting mortality, and I found my thoughts wavering between the miraculous views and a miracle needed for Carol.

We took an off-road Jeep tour. The tour guide had a mug of coffee in one hand while he used the other to steer over rock formations. My fascination was less with the scenery and more with his uncanny ability not to slosh any of the java over the mug's rim. One of the passengers asked a question I couldn't hear, but the tour guide's answer was clear. He had moved to Sedona from Maine to help relieve the symptoms of his wife's illness. He ended the response by saying she had passed away four years earlier.

It was a poignant moment, because I carried the secret that Carol had FTD. She never appeared to understand the diagnosis, and I had not and never would explain it to her. There was no benefit for her to comprehend it even if she could. She was happy, and I was caring for her, and that was all that mattered.

The next day we explored trails in an ATV and, the following day, took a four-hour train ride on Verde Canyon Railroad from Clarkdale to Perkinsville and back. I've long forgotten the other routes and images of the two days but distinctly remember Carol's smile as we drove along highways and local roads in our coupe convertible. It was the smile you saw when a person was lost in beauty.

I admit that the rock scenery and evergreen vegetation of Sedona had regenerative and inspirational effects. I found the red-orange rock visually stimulating and did feel a sense of renewal. The trails and overlooks inspired contemplation for me.

One day, a group of elderly women from New York were seated next to us in a restaurant. They had returned for a visit in memory of a friend who took the trip with them a year earlier, knowing she would die within months from a terminal illness. At times, I could make out what they were saying; at other times, their words were absorbed in the din of the dining room, and all I could hear were raucous outbursts of laughter. They were celebrating their friend's life.

FTD presented new realities for me on the trip. I couldn't leave Carol alone in the room for fear of her walking out and becoming lost or overwhelmed by the new surroundings. Since I was responsible for her, I lost some freedoms I would have enjoyed like going for a jog, making use of the spa, or taking a nap.

I became aware that should I be injured or become ill, Carol could not properly notify someone, coordinate arrangements to manage the situation, care for herself, or alert the kids back home. This became my preoccupation during our stay, and the vacation also made me more aware of her dependency on me for day-to-day living. Considering all this, I made the hotel manager aware of our circumstances. Fortunately, it never became an issue.

Importantly, the trip reinforced my goal to cure my anxiety. I wanted to find a way to improve my life while making other lives better in the process, particularly Carol's life, and find a purpose beyond myself. It happened on the final day of our stay.

Look, Up in the Sky! It's A...

We drove an hour to the launching pad of the helicopter tour of the Grand Canyon while playing Carol's favorite songs along the way.

The helicopter pilot was ex-military. He commanded attention from his passengers, corrected our ignorance, barked directions at us, and sliced the air with facts as efficiently as the rotor blades that whirled above us. He was a hardened fellow, the kind who seemed to resent his job and whose anger was revealed by a bulging vein on his forehead. He reminded me of a taunting remark I use with my kids: "I don't know why people have become so angry, but I do wish they'd be happy about it." My kids don't think it is clever, but I have fun goading them.

I asked the pilot if he could arrange to have Carol sit next to him so she could have the best view of the landscape through the massive window in the front of the helicopter. I gave him some background on her situation and relayed that she had been talking up her excitement about the flight for weeks. His demeanor melted in an instant, and as he made the arrangements, my opinion of him did the same. He made sure to seat me next to her.

It was an adrenaline rush, flying across the deepest and widest part of the canyon. From our vantage point, we saw the powerful flow of the Colorado River and how the carving of the huge canyon over millions of years was made possible by such force. The buttes and mesas rose sharply from a flat landscape in incredible formations that were formed through weathering and erosion. I pointed these out repeatedly to Carol, admittedly beyond the point of usefulness.

The one thing you become aware of in a helicopter is the precariousness of life. You realize that a mechanical failure of the engine is like having a magic carpet yanked from under you, the result being an immediate plunge, and ours would be fifteen hundred feet or more onto hostile terrain. A clarity of purpose came to me. I experienced an overwhelming sense of powerlessness that brought me face to face with my mortality. I completely let go of trying to control the "what if" scenarios of mechanical failure and was able to enjoy the sights, ride, pilot's observations, and Carol's company with great awareness and clarity.

It was as if I was witnessing my fear, and this had the effect of fading it until it was gone. The absence of fear and anxiety allowed me to be present in the moment, aware and mindful, not distracted by ruminations on the past or worries about the future. I was calm. I had evenness of mind.

I had the sense that if the helicopter plummeted and at the same time someone served my favorite ice cream, I would remain in the moment with my attention on the treat, not the impending tragedy. Since it was impossible to change a plunge to earth, I had the awareness to enjoy each remaining second of life. I finally felt equanimity, the total release of control I had been searching for most of my life.

It seems the hardest part of knowing who we are is learning where to look. If I could find a way back to this state of awareness permanently, it seemed my anxiety would be cured. This consciousness showed that I could live in the moment and without fear. Because I had experienced this awareness, I knew it was possible to experience it again, but I needed a method.

After we landed, Carol wanted a souvenir picture of us with the pilot in front of the helicopter, a copy of a video of our flight, and a sweatshirt with a helicopter logo. Her look of contentment made our one-hour highway drive back to the hotel in forty-five-degree weather with the convertible top down, heat cranked up, jackets zipped, fluffy scarves tightened, and hats pulled down over our ears worth it all. I was especially grateful for the heated seats and heated steering wheel.

Quality of Life

When we got back to our room, I wrote down my goal to find a method that would help me to duplicate the awareness and equanimity I experienced while flying above the Grand Canyon. I'd written down goals throughout my forty years as a businessman and believed it engraved the goals in my mind, and by reviewing them on occasion, they were made tangible rather than abstract. Writing and visualizing goals turned them into a living force. It sent out positive energy, which helped them manifest. It opened my mind so that I saw connections to people and events I would have likely overlooked had I not written them.

Out of the seemingly thousands of thoughts I had each day, my goals stood out because they had significance. I visualized the results I wanted, which allowed me to emotionally connect with the goal. Over time, this simple act produced results and was transformative. I used this method in my personal and professional lives, and I continue using it to this day. We should choose our thoughts wisely, considering that they can nourish our souls or poison them.

I thought that achieving higher awareness would lessen my emotional pain and deepen my reservoir for compassion, and this subtle change would transfer to Carol and improve the quality of our lives. I saw it as another expression of Newton's third law of motion. What is true in the physical world is true in the spiritual world.

As the year progressed, so did Carol's need for direct care. Caring for someone who couldn't care for themselves was a reward of its own but also stressful. One minute I'd be working at my job, and the next, I'd be making her lunch, taking her for a walk, or taking her to the bathroom. I was fortunate that she enjoyed watching TV, as it minimized the downtime with my business. I would watch her from my office with the cameras I had installed in our home.

Caregiving affected my life in myriad unforeseen ways. It began to cut off my social interactions with friends and family. My freedom became restricted in that I had to plan for someone to be with her for even the most basic activities like getting a haircut, going to the gym or a doctor's appointment, or visiting a customer.

Carol's friends began to drift away, and there were fewer calls to see how she was doing. I felt more isolated as family and friends pulled back from us or because we could spend only a certain amount of time with them before Carol became restless and we had to leave. I detected an uneasiness when people were with us, an awkwardness, like they forgot how to speak in our presence. I convinced myself that people were having difficulty accepting the disease or were uncomfortable with it.

I had decided to care for Carol in our home rather than a care facility shortly after her diagnosis, feeling it was best for her quality of life. Memories from periods of her past were associated with our home as well as with her accomplishments, the surroundings, and my companionship. No one has a more personal stake in the well-being and care of an FTD patient than those who love them. They are fragile and vulnerable physically and mentally.

I spent five years selling medical products to nurse directors at long-term care and assisted living facilities. I spent two years creating an institutional pharmacy company that provided patient medications to some of these same facilities. During this time, I witnessed the staff's lack of focus on dementia patients. Some had inadequate knowledge and training, but there were practices that were detrimental to people living with dementia such as relying solely on antipsychotics for managing behavior. Some of the facilities even had confusing and unsafe environments. I'm not making a statement about institutional care, only about what I observed in many of the facilities I was in.

While compromised care wasn't true for all facilities, it was widespread enough for me to take notice. The reality was that caregivers in institutional settings were typically at the low end of the pay scale, facilities were often understaffed, employees were overworked, and the workforce was stressed by the responsibilities of their jobs.

The one thing that all FTD patients need is compassion, and compassion can't be bought at any price. Be it love or misery, compassion or bitterness—that which prevails in the hearts and minds of people will prevail in their surroundings.

I understand there are many reasons that people must rely on institutional settings for dementia care, and not all facilities are inadequate. I am not disparaging the medical industry. It's simply that my insights and experiences brought me to a conclusion to provide Carol's care at home, and I am blessed to work from home, so I can do it.

Up, Up, and Away

It was a sunny day in July 2019 as we climbed into a large wicker basket tethered to a blue-and-green hot air balloon. We rose from a field of undulating grass and traveled where the wind took us over parts of Warren County, New Jersey. We had a bird's-eye view of wildlife, forests, farmland, and the distant silhouette of New York City. I felt a sensation of weightlessness as we drifted over a landscape that stretched for miles. The pilot controlled the balloon's height with burner thrusts from propane gas. I felt each blast of intense heat on my face and shoulders, and with every lunge, we climbed higher.

The idea for a balloon ride was Carol's, and she enjoyed each moment, fearlessly taking pictures. I took pictures too but admit it was done faintheartedly. We floated over people's homes, and many ran outdoors to wave at our spectacle. As we approached a major highway, the altitude allowed us to see miles of cars slowing and weaving as occupants stretched their heads out their windows to see us. The line of cars looked like the long, flattened, many-segmented body of a centipede winding its way toward us.

The scenery below looked like an enormous garden of trees, a leafy paradise supported by antler-like branches. They gave the air the aroma of a freshly baked pie.

I believe trees have consciousness, as do the creatures I watched from the train traveling past the marshlands. There is intelligence, purposeful design, and a system of interdependence that sustains life within the workings of ecosystems. There is evidence of consciousness in trees in the way they compete against each other for space and light. There must be an inborn awareness in a tree to know that it must compete for survival.

I talked with a forester who told of an area that went through a heavy drought, and in the following years, the trees that had suffered through scarcity consumed less water in the spring so that they had more available for the summer months. To me, this is proof that trees can learn, choose, and remember. There is awareness.

In a book I authored on conservation, I give an example of how the jack pine and lodgepole pine adapt to survive wildfires. These trees were part of an ecosystem that was prone to fire, and their survival was threatened. Over time, they created a process that made them dependent on the fire that threatened their existence. The tree's recognition of intense heat triggers seed release and enables germination. Fire now causes the reproduction that sustains the species.

I think that such adaptations have their roots in consciousness. There must be awareness for the jack pine and lodgepole to adapt to their changing world. Adapting to avoid a threat demonstrates an understanding of the need to change what is to what is needed, which is evidence of consciousness.

That moment in the helicopter, when the fear of death left me temporarily and I was living in the moment, brought me closer to seeing this consciousness in all living things. I saw purpose on a grand scale, and this reinforced the idea that I might find purpose on a grand scale in what Carol and I were going through. Maybe it could provide perspective and soften my pain.

Sunflowers, Hamburgers, and Big Butts

We had driven to the hot air balloon launch site in a Jeep Wrangler with the convertible top down to view the countryside and rolling hills. Carol's love for open-air driving had started years before with a preowned Jeep that I bought. She never said why she liked it so much, but maybe it was her way of prioritizing fun over a lifetime of spoiling her practical side. Maybe it was because she could smell nature instead of stale, chilled conditioned air. Maybe because it bettered a beautiful day, or maybe it was to share her shining face with the world.

We'd drop the Jeep's convertible top in late spring, summer, and early fall to ride to the Jersey shore to a seafood restaurant overlooking Sandy Hook Bay. We'd watch countless boats fishing for fluke, bluefish, or striped bass and enjoyed the warm breeze coming off the Atlantic Ocean. We took a forty-five-minute drive every night over the back roads near our home with music at high volume, the convertible top up or down as required.

As her FTD progressed, I found our drive together was one link that allowed us to still feel connected. It was truly quality time.

In the fall of 2019, I took Carol for a drive to see a sunflower farm. I was trying to think of ways to change her routines and keep her engaged in life. A sunflower was like a dose of sunshine, so I thought it was good timing. The farm was 130 acres of sunflowers, pumpkins, a corn maze, and areas to pick blueberries, raspberries, and lavender. We were there about twenty minutes when she told me she was ready to return home. She was showing increasing signs of impulsiveness at this point as the FTD progressed and she had difficulty concentrating. Perhaps this played into her decision to leave.

Other changes were beginning to appear. Carol always loved when our children visited, and they couldn't stay long enough to make her happy. We always heard disappointment in her voice when she had to say goodbye to them. This was beginning to change. Not long after their arrival, she would say with the honesty of a child that they needed to go. There was such a beautiful innocence to her demand that no one was offended by it. In fact, it filled the room with laughter.

When we went shopping, Carol needed to touch things in the store and sometimes straighten items on the shelves. Waiting in line to pay a cashier seemed to be her favorite spot, since she had all kinds of candy within reach. I was careful not to turn away from her, because I knew when I turned back, she'd have a half-eaten candy bar in her hand and the balance causing her cheeks to bulge as she chewed.

She started asking me every day if I wanted to go to what became her favorite burger restaurant, Burger Brothers. She hadn't been a hamburger fan, but she was now a convert. She asked several times a day, "Hey, do you want to go to Burger Brothers?" Each time, she asked with the wonder and excitement of a kid who thought they had just found a cure for boredom.

Some of her symptoms were comical. As her inhibition faded, she felt no hesitation telling people that they had "big butts." If the silhouette warranted it, she told them. No one escaped her childlike honesty whether it was a visitor to our home or some unsuspecting soul in a doctor's waiting area. One time, my daughter was telling us she gained too much weight, and when she paused to hear reassurances that her concerns were unfounded, Carol piped up, "You have a big butt." It was such an innocent and disarming response that we all burst out laughing. Often FTD can bring out the worst of human nature, but we were fortunate that it was no match for Carol's happy heart and bright demeanor.

As easy as it was to find innocence, comedy, and endearment in some changes that took place in Carol, others were painful. She was remarkably close with her mother and used to call her every night, but she stopped even asking about her. Carol used to spend an hour on the phone with her sister on Sundays, but the calls became brief because of her inability to engage in activity for lengthy periods.

Carol lost interest in keeping our house clean, making dinner, and making the bed, and she no longer washed our clothes. I used to tease her about there being an "armoire fairy" in our home, because the dirty clothes I tossed in the hamper would magically return clean, folded, smelling wonderful, and neatly stacked in my armoire. She giggled when I said it, because she knew it was my way of thanking her. Now I am happily the "armoire fairy" for both of us.

I was overseeing her bathing routine, because she missed cleaning some areas, and I would carefully point them out. It was important for her to continue doing things on her own, as it kept her mind active. I began to take her for manicures and pedicures. At times, her restlessness made it difficult for her to sit still, but the nail technicians were wonderfully patient.

X-Ray Decision

Annual checkups with Carol's general practitioner, gynecologist, and dentist were becoming a challenge because her impulsivity and impatience made her walk around waiting areas. She was still able to follow most of the directives the medical professionals gave her, but their lack of expertise with FTD patients was visible by their timidity and awkwardness in handling her. They stared at me when they asked her to say or do something. This point was driven home during her mammogram screening.

Carol had just walked into the area where they performed x-rays, and I remained in a large waiting area. She was there for a six-month checkup; the doctor was concerned about a growth she wanted to closely monitor.

I picked up a magazine and was flipping through the pages when a short woman wearing a name tag on the traditional doctor's white coat approached. Her face was small and centered by a proportional nose and tiny mouth. Her almond-shaped eyes looked downward as she neared me and then lifted to look at me at the edge of my personal space. She introduced herself as Carol's radiology doctor. After a quick round of pleasantries, she apologetically said she couldn't perform the mammogram because her assistants were having difficulty positioning Carol in front of the x-ray machine. The doctor left a gaping pause at the end of her sentence where I had expected her to provide a solution. I recognized the pause was her way of telling me there was no solution, so I instinctively offered to help.

The smiles I got from women as I entered the mammogram area weren't flirtatious but contemptuous. They reminded me of one I got from a manager at a private club when he informed me of the decision to decline my membership. The two technicians I was introduced to were pleasant and helpful.

Helping Carol with her mammogram was a sad and difficult undertaking, though she was obliviously happy. The trouble was that as soon as the technicians tried to position her in front of the x-ray machine and place her breast between the firm surfaces, the posture needed was so unnatural that Carol instinctively pushed away to maintain her balance every time they tried to position her. I calmly explained to her what the assistants wanted done as I stood behind her, inelegantly rotating and bending her body into position using my hands, hip, and the upper part of my thigh. After the first attempt, I decided to play her favorite music on my iPhone and joked with her, trying to make it a fun experience, though I doubt that any woman would use the words fun and mammogram in the same sentence. It took us forty-five minutes to complete the x-rays.

Tying Up Loose Ends

During this period, I began to miss Carol's personality terribly even though she was still physically with me, and I was fully aware the disease would worsen. I didn't talk about these feelings with friends or family because they lacked understanding, which made their sympathy seem misplaced.

In addition to my grieving, caregiving was becoming stressful and emotional, but it seemed oddly offset by knowing that I was making a difference in the quality of Carol's life. It was as if the gift of giving myself to her was a gift coming back to me in equal measure. It was a gift that needed no appreciation from her. Caring for Carol connected us on a deep, unspoken level and brought me closer to her.

Caregiving was becoming all-consuming, and I was still running my home-based business. I had heard stories about caregivers who were family members and became discouraged, suffered burnout, and neglected their own health. I was concerned that high levels of stress could trigger my depression, panic attacks, and agoraphobia. I was experiencing sadness, anxiety, and loneliness. Caring for a person with FTD was a series of grief experiences over the passage of time, and I watched shared memories disappear and skills wear away. It was confusing and frustrating.

There were also growing financial responsibilities. Dr. Devi's practice did not take medical insurance, so all the office visits and TMS treatments were paid out of pocket. Dr. Devi suggested I should plan for ten to twenty years of care. This made me consider costs and planning for the future including ongoing medical treatment, medical equipment for other conditions, prescription drugs, in-home care, personal care supplies, and other possible costs. I couldn't anticipate the exact costs, but planning gave me an approximate idea of what I might need.

Carol and I met with an attorney and had him create several legal papers for us. A durable power of attorney (POA) designated who would make healthcare decisions when we could no longer do so. Living wills recorded our wishes for medical treatment near the end of life or if we were not able to make decisions about emergency treatment. Do Not Resuscitate (DNR) orders instructed healthcare professionals not to perform CPR if the heart stopped beating. A legal will indicated how our assets and estate should be distributed.

I completed the Practitioner Orders for Life-Sustaining Treatment (POLST) form. It was a planning tool that empowered people to collaborate closely with their medical team and detail their personal goals and medical preferences when facing a serious illness, helped with end-of-life care planning, and stated a person's goals about care and medical preferences. A completed POLST form was an order that became part of a medical record.

THE YEAR 2020

We're Not Lost (We Just Don't Know Where We Are)

In the spring of 2020, Carol's behavioral changes continued. FTD affected behavior, decision making, and personality, and her decline was noticeable across all three areas. She began compulsively picking nail polish off her fingernails and habitually rubbing the tip of the nail on her index finger along her pants, eventually wearing through the fabric and exposing skin.

There were changes in her dietary habits, the most prominent being her attraction to sweet treats. She was binge eating and gaining weight, so I was forced to hide food to help manage her impulses. I found the bingeing a challenge to manage, since any food left on the counter or not secured in the refrigerator would disappear. I heard on a program about a woman who hid food from her husband with FTD for the same reason, but this worked only for a brief period, as his compulsion caused him to go into a neighbor's home and eat their food. The woman worked out a strategy with the neighbor to prevent him from entering their home, but he snuck out to the nearest convenience store, took food from the shelves, and ate it.

I noticed Carol having difficulty regulating the shower handle for the hot and cold water. She couldn't find the temperature she wanted, so I marked the wall so she could know the spot for her preferred temperature. I noticed that after washing her hair, she wasn't rinsing thoroughly, so I began to help her with this. One day, she exited the shower and put on her underwear before drying herself. I began reminding her to use a towel.

We took daily walks at a nearby park, and I started to hear her whispering numbers as she counted each step. One summer day, the temperature was 80 degrees, and as we left our home, she put on her winter coat. Carol enjoyed her routines, one of which was to manage my incoming and outgoing mail. One day, she reminded me that there were no stamps on two of the outgoing envelopes. I assumed that she corrected the oversight and put the envelopes in our mailbox. The postal carrier took the mail to the post office, but the letters were returned for insufficient postage, as Carol never put stamps on them.

One afternoon, Carol had gone upstairs to our bedroom, which was unusual but not a cause for concern. I was curious, and after a few minutes, I called out and asked what she was doing. She replied she was watching TV. I was surprised because from where I was standing, I could usually hear the TV. I went upstairs and found her sitting on our bed staring at the TV, but it wasn't turned on.

She was beginning to have difficulty swallowing. One day, she put pills in her mouth and instead of sipping water to swallow them, she treated them as if they were chewable. I couldn't imagine how dry and bitter they must have tasted, but she had no reaction. I began crushing all her medicines and mixed them in yogurt for her to eat.

I also saw she was putting food in her mouth faster than she could chew and swallow. She then hoarded the accumulating food in her bulging cheeks and sometimes forgot to finish chewing. I began feeding her softer foods. If I served chicken, I cut it into tiny pieces, which resolved the problem.

One day, when Anthony Jr. and I were in the kitchen, Carol walked in and began talking with us. In midsentence, I noticed her bend slightly at the waist, and her knees came together and touched. At this point, she had difficulty controlling her need to urinate, so I began buying products to manage urinary incontinence.

I had suggested to Carol that she stop driving, and she agreed without me having to provide an explanation. It wasn't that she couldn't navigate roads and understand her location, but she had no tolerance while waiting for red lights or stop signs. I thought that the matter was resolved.

There was a day I came downstairs from my office and noticed the back door open and our car missing. I was terrified she might have had an accident and didn't know where to begin looking for her. I was almost paralyzed by fear, and dread twisted my gut. I rushed to get the keys to our other car, and just as I ran into the garage, I saw her driving down the driveway. It was a great relief, and the fact that she hit the side of the garage while entering, leaving a wide streak of white paint on the bumper, became a happy consequence of her arrival home.

For as long as I could remember, Carol's routine was to go to bed at 9:00 p.m., but now she was doing so at 8:30 p.m. I remained downstairs, and she would text me to join her at some point. After decades of marriage, I thought it was adorable that she would text me to come to bed. Even though it was a bit earlier than the time I wanted to go to bed, I always accommodated her.

One day, the texts stopped and never reappeared. I missed them, as I missed all the fragments of Carol's personality that were forever gone. FTD was complicating my grieving. It was making her less psychologically present though she remained physically present with hands-on needs for care. Our settled relationship was being replaced by uncertainty, which complicated my ability to process the loss, grieve, and think about moving forward with my life. The changes were gradual. I knew that Carol was who she had always been, but at the same time, she wasn't who she once was.

FTD presents intangibles, and lines are blurred. It's not the same grief I experienced with the loss of my mother. Her loss was clearly defined and final, and I understood mourning. FTD occurs slowly and in bits and pieces over time, so feeling the loss of Carol's charm, her ability to problem solve, her humor, her relationship with our children, our shared memories, and the intimacy of our relationship recurs as the disease progresses. I find the many changes over a brief period of time anguishing and have difficulty making sense of what is happening.

For me, major life transitions seem to create severe stress, which also seems to trigger depression and panic attacks. The stress I am under is magnified because Carol relies on me for her health, well-being, and care, which means that me getting sick is not an option. She needs me to get her out of bed in the morning, tuck her into bed at night, and everything in between.

Anthony P. Mauro Sr.

The financial uncertainty that came with a long-term disease like FTD caused me to continue working at my business while caring for her. Though I was managing the situation capably, I was concerned about having a mental health crisis like the one I had at twenty-five years old. The prospect added to the pressure I felt. I wished there was a book on how to handle all these challenges.

Sometimes the only book to guide us through adversity is the one we write as we make our way through it.

Anthony Jr. and Gina's Wedding

On the afternoon of August 29, I took Carol's arm, and we were introduced as part of Anthony Jr. and Gina's wedding party. We made our way to the head of the reception area, and Carol was excited and happy about the celebration. As with Tori's wedding two years earlier, Carol couldn't participate in any of the planning, and the FTD noticeably progressed. She wasn't dancing as much, and when she did, it was with less mobility, but she was enjoying herself and getting plenty of attention from friends and family.

At this point, I had learned enough about FTD to adjust my expectations and realize that sudden, unpredicted changes might take place. I knew that daily living routines could be upended as I accommodated Carol's declining medical, physical, and emotional condition. My approach to the wedding was to keep things as normal and upbeat as possible without putting any pressure on Carol.

I suggested a wedding gift idea to Carol, and she gave her approval, though I don't know the degree to which she understood the decision we were making. I did the same with the flowers for the ceremony. We both signed the wedding card. I liked making a fuss over Carol and keeping her involved in decisions, as I could see in her eyes and by her smile that it made her feel important, and this kept hope and joy alive in her and in all of us.

It was an outside wedding, and the skies were angry and threatening. It rained most of the day, but nature's gift to the bride and groom was perfect weather for the start of the ceremony. At the end of the reception, the rain fell again. Anthony Jr. and Gina had put together the budget and managed all the details of the meaningful gala, and the results were grand.

The most nostalgic moment was when Anthony Jr. danced with his mom. It was his symbol of love and respect for her, and it created a special moment for everyone in attendance. It proved that a heart could be filled with joy and sorrow at the same time. I stood next to Tori, who was weeping, and it took all my efforts to not do the same. In the end, the day was dazzling, the bride was radiant, and the groom delighted in all of it.

A Few Less Pieces

It was now taking a long time for Carol to finish her food. She would take a bite, become impatient, get up from the table, and walk around the kitchen before sitting down for the next bite. Sometimes she would say she had to pee, which inevitably was not the case but likely due to restlessness, which was worsening over time.

Carol used to love iced tea, but she didn't ask for it any longer. One day, as we were headed outside, she placed the strap of her pocketbook over her shoulder and then put her coat on over it. The coat bulged. She looked down at it and then raised her eyes to meet mine as if asking for a way out of the predicament, so I assisted.

For as long as we had been married, when Carol stepped out of the shower, she bundled her hair in a plush towel. Early on, I asked her why, and she had said that it prevented dripping and breakage and gave her healthier hair. It seemed a simple and relaxing routine for her. For whatever reason, the practice stopped.

Our Days Are Merry

As the winter holidays approached, I wanted to make sure our rich, meaningful traditions continued. It was a time of year for togetherness, sharing, laughter, and making memories, and I wanted to emphasize this for the kids over sadness and stress.

I went to the basement to rummage through boxes of decorations, most of which we'd collected since our first Christmas together: bells, candles, garlands, a snow globe with a winter scene, angels, pinecones, and hanging ornaments our kids made when they were in elementary school. I put up the centerpiece that would give all the adornments their meaningful sparkle: the Christmas tree.

I played Carol's favorite Christmas CDs. She had a selection that provided an air of nostalgia and also a determined optimism for times to come. I admit that decorating the tree was more than digging into an assortment of ornaments. It took skill, since it helped to set the tone for the rest of the house, and while I understand the notion, I was clumsy with my choices. I always relied on Carol. I tried to give the tree extra verve by using a mix of shapes, texture, and pop from mirrored and iridescent accents, but when I stepped back to look at the big picture, it fell flat of the flair that Carol always added. We were at a new place in our lives, and I realized that this was one more area in which I would have to adapt, and with a second look, our decorated home took on a new kind of beauty.

I asked Carol to help me cook her favorite baked ziti recipe, a Christmas tradition with our family. I found her old, tattered, stained index card with the recipe, spread the ingredients widely across the kitchen counter, and followed the sequence of adding fixings. I'd never made baked ziti and in fact hadn't cooked a meal since before we were married. Though I didn't duplicate the marvelous results of my wife's cooking, I did add the joy of Christmas as an ingredient.

I had Carol help with wrapping gifts by placing her finger on the ribbons so I could tie the bows and set each present under the tree. We watched her favorite Christmas movies on the days leading up to December 25 including *Polar Express, A Charlie Brown Christmas, Arthur Christmas*, and *White Christmas*. I wasn't trying to make the perfect Christmas, simply trying to maintain our routine for the holiday and make it a source of pleasure for everyone as best I could.

Though I made sure 2020 ended with a ray of holiday sunshine for the family, it was a bitterly cold year personally. I was grieving but confused. Grieving usually happened after a death, but I was going through it before death happened. I felt sadness and exhaustion. I was grieving the loss of Carol's abilities, of hope, of the stability in our lives, of our future, of the plans we had made, of her reasoning ability, and of a sense of security.

Each of these losses seemed like a metaphor for the transition from fall to winter and a tree's ritual of losing leaves. At first the change is subtle as the leaves slowly change color, and then a few lose their grip and twirl to the ground. You don't notice the newly opened space they left behind, but you know the ritual of autumn has begun. One day, you recognize a covering of leaves scattered around the base of the tree and look up to see rays of light pass through the empty spaces where they once clung. The loss is made apparent, but it is gradual. A wind howls, and a mass of leaves lose their grip and expose a skeleton of limbs, branches, and twigs, except for the most defiant stragglers, but they too eventually succumb to the inevitable.

I had never experienced this type of grief. I wasn't even sure if it was grief or if I was a tangled mess of emotions and clueless as to how to unravel myself. To complicate matters, I thought I was the only person in the world to experience this suffering.

I let the optimist and pessimist prattle over a half-filled glass: I am the pragmatist and see the matter as settled by drinking what is in the glass and ordering another round. I entered the new year determined to get to the root of my anxiety and suffering and begin to exhaust them.

THE YEAR 2021
(FIRST HALF)

White Men Can Jump

In modern America, people prefer going places by car. There is a sense of freedom while driving, and a car gives you control, allowing you to choose your times and routes. These reasons have an appeal over trains, taxis, and subways, all of which we used last year.

I switched from rail to our sedan due to an incident in a New York City subway station on our way to Carol's doctor appointment. I was becoming aware that should something serious like a medical emergency happen to me, Carol would be at the mercy of subway surroundings. Every time we traveled, there were mentally ill riders seeking refuge on subway cars. On a few occasions, we had sellers approach us with illegal drugs. The area of New Jersey in which I grew up is considered part of metropolitan New York City, so I was accustomed to the surroundings, but I became uneasy after I purchased a MetroCard (a card swiped at the turnstile to pay the fare) in Herald Square station.

I had just purchased two cards. Carol got to the turnstile immediately before me, so I swiped her card as I stood behind her. As I swiped, she pushed the waist-high turnstile, and it spun, leaving her on the other side and in the subway train area. I swiped my card, but the turnstile remained locked. I swiped my card again and pushed the turnstile bar, but it wouldn't budge. I looked up and saw that Carol was about fifteen feet away from me. Her attention was caught by a person who had set up a cheap folding table. I was overcome with worry and swiped again with the same results. By now, Carol was talking with the man and removing her wallet from her handbag. I was afraid the wallet would be stolen. After another unsuccessful swipe, I jumped over the turnstile and got to her before she had a chance to hand over the wallet.

From that moment on, I drove us to her doctors appointments. As confident as I was driving the traffic-packed streets, with the crisscrossing of fearless pedestrians and being startled by passing delivery bikers rushing food to impatient customers, there were times I felt I could use the help of a city survival guide. Finding a place to park on the street was as uncommon as winning a lottery, and trying to find a reasonably priced parking garage was a game that combined treasure hunting with solving a jigsaw puzzle.

These frustrations were compounded when driving with a passenger with FTD. One day after leaving an appointment, I was driving on Ninth Avenue, stuck in the flow of crazed drivers and the roll, pitch, and yaw of stop-and-go cars jockeying for street positions. Carol must have decided that she'd had enough of the ruckus and opened her door to get out and walk.

I had visions of the car door being torn off its hinges by a driver with anger issues. Flooded with a wave of adrenaline, I reached across the console and Carol with the speed of a boxer's jab to close the door before it flung wide open.

A Faint Memory

About one month later, when we returned home from an appointment in New York City, I pulled into our garage and said in a gratified tone, "We're home." Carol turned to me, smiled, clapped her hands, and got out of the car. I was fumbling with the keys, trying to find the one that opened the back door, as she rounded the rear of the car and walked toward me. I looked up into her eyes and noticed a distant look. Her legs began to wobble, and then she collapsed. I rushed to her, not knowing the cause or whether she had hit her head on the concrete floor. Her eyes remained open during the episode, which lasted only a few seconds. She was able to get back on her feet almost immediately, and fortunately, she wasn't injured.

After this incident, a few more fainting-like episodes occurred and then stopped as mysteriously as they had appeared. It was disturbing to witness, because I was looking into Carol's open eyes, and she appeared to be conscious though she couldn't speak or move. Dr. Devi believed it had more to do with the medicine she was taking, and a dosage adjustment made the episodes disappear.

I noticed important memories beginning to fade. She no longer remembered the birthdays of our children and even got mine wrong, though she remembered the month correctly. One night as I took her upstairs to bed, I went into her closet to get her nightie, and when I turned to undress her, she had gotten into bed with her clothes still on.

In the back of my mind, I watched for an important measure of the degenerative progress: Carol forgetting her handbag. I admit it was my own odd benchmark, but I knew that Carol and her handbag were like indivisible twins. It seemed more than a place to keep important personal effects and almost seemed to satisfy a deep psychological need to organize, which was second nature to her.

One evening, we were preparing to take our daily ride in the Jeep and were going through our preparation routine: Carol grabbed her handbag and slung the strap over her shoulder as I gathered my keys, put my wallet in my back pocket, and roamed the house, complaining that I couldn't find my iPhone. We completed our routine, and I walked her to the Jeep, but as I helped fasten her seat belt, I noticed that she had left her handbag in the house. She would not remember her handbag from that point forward, regardless of where we were. I felt I had witnessed the loss of a big piece of her, and it was a painful indicator of the FTD progression.

There was more evidence that Carol's awareness was narrowing. The one other item that she had a strong connection to was her iPhone. She carried it wherever she went or had it next to her on an end table or nightstand. She used it to see where her kids were on the Find My app or play songs from her music playlist. Her favorite song was "Peace Train" by Cat Stevens.

There seemed to be power in music for her. She couldn't express whether it stimulated memories, made her calmer, or boosted her mood, but as an observer, I'd say it did all three. There was a magical connection; music had a pervasive effect and went beyond entertainment. It was as if she absorbed the frequencies and syllables of the sounds and lyrics. There was delight in her eyes, and she sang and clapped energetically to the beat. Fascinatingly, she knew the lyrics to some of the most obscure songs.

Although she had a bond with the iPhone, she was losing her ability to use Find My and music apps. She tapped on them too quickly, which deleted them. I'd download them again and set them up only to find they had disappeared within a day or two. She began pressing on apps that caught her attention but didn't know what to do once they were open, or she'd call people by randomly tapping their phone number from her contact list. They'd usually answer with a confused "Hello?" not expecting to receive a call from Carol, but she wouldn't say anything, because she didn't realize she had made a call. One morning at 4:30 a.m., I was awakened by the familiar FaceTime ringtone. I sat up in bed and turned to see her playing with her phone. She had mistakenly reached her brother on FaceTime.

Despite the heartbreak and hardship that came with FTD, I saw a blessing in Carol's condition. A lifetime of goodness served her at this stage. Her eyes lit up every morning when I woke her, and when I asked how she slept, she said with delight, "I slept good!" I was grateful that she still knew me. She laughed and giggled throughout the day in a sweet, almost childlike way. She found humor in so many things, most of which were apparent only to her, but to live in unremitting happiness is a goal for most of us, and Carol seemed to have found it.

She got up in the morning with wholehearted outbursts of rhythmic clapping, and they continued throughout the day until she rested her head on her pillow at night. She was alive with enthusiasm, easy going, and cheerful, which had a great deal of charm and left us happy to be around her. When I started singing a song, she chimed in, knowing more of the words than I did. Her sunny demeanor didn't lessen the pain of watching her go through FTD, but it allowed my family to see past the agony to find humor and love.

At this point, Carol no longer processed that she needed to wear proper clothing to walk in the rain or frigid temperatures or that the weather was too severe to even go outside. When we took our walk, she would pause a few seconds every ten feet and then resume walking. She clapped joyfully and loudly in restaurants and stores, often turning heads in the process before people realized something was wrong and then returned to whatever they were doing. When in retail stores, she occasionally stopped to neaten items on shelves or was happy to snatch and eat a candy bar before I noticed and could stop her. Secretly, I was happy for her triumph.

One afternoon, we were in an Italian specialty store, and I was waiting at the deli with Carol next to me. As I placed my order, she noticed a shopping cart next to us and began pushing it as if it was ours. The owner of the cart was within eye distance, and she said nothing while giving me a glance that showed she understood. I gently redirected Carol and thanked the woman for her kindness.

We're All in This Together

In October of last year, I took Carol to a huge farm to pick pumpkins. There was an enclosed area with a wide opening that had pumpkins displayed on wooden frames, forming a small house that looked like it was made of pumpkins. I wanted to get a picture of her standing in the doorway to send to our kids.

An older woman sat on a weather-beaten chair at the entrance. She looked tired, as if she was at the end of a shift that had drained her energy. I could tell by the way she was leaning that if she were to stand, she would be bent and crooked. I nodded as we passed by, and she stopped us. I looked into her dark eyes that were shadowed by deep furrows on her forehead as she squinted from the noon sun. She told me there was a fee to enter.

As I reached into my pocket, she looked at Carol, back at me, and said, "Please, no need to pay. We're all in this together." She must have noticed Carol's condition. It was a loving act. Love is a phenomenon of life: it costs nothing but is priceless, it cannot be touched but touches everyone, and the more we use it to lift ourselves, the more it helps to lift others.

About this time, I started to pursue a way to duplicate the joy, freedom, and awareness I had flying above the Grand Canyon in the helicopter. I read about Hinduism again, but it was faith based, and I was looking for something that was spiritual but not necessarily an institutionalized religion. I am by no means an atheist. As far as I am concerned, an atheist is like a fish that doesn't believe in the existence of the sea because it has never seen it. I already had my faith. Instead, I was looking for a technique, a practice I could use to elevate consciousness by using my anguish and anxieties to raise my awareness.

It wasn't long after this that I came upon an article about the temporariness of life, and it started me thinking about how I tried to live a stabile life: set schedules, routines, be in control of things. Stability gave me a sense of comfort and order, but when it was disrupted or things happened that were beyond my control, it created anxiety, sorrow, or torment. FTD was making me understand that the essence of life was not stability but change. By trying to maintain stability and control things that were uncontrollable, I was working against the essence of life and waging an unwinnable campaign.

Change had always felt like an abnormal disruption, but I was seeing that it was an integral part of life. Friendships faded away, school began and ended, families moved, there were marriages and divorces, illness, new jobs, retirement, buying and selling a house. Babies were born, and people died. I noticed that there were changes each second of every day, some nuanced and others painfully difficult. Life was in a constant state of transition. For me, the natural extension of this fact was to find a way to feel comfortable with change.

Everything Changes

One day, I typed the word *change* in my search engine, and the synonym *impermanence* was highlighted, so I pursued the word further. As I thought about impermanence, I began to see that tastes, smells, sounds, sights, emotions, physical feelings, and my thoughts were impermanent. I started developing my thinking about impermanent things and realized that even the solar system was changing through expansion. Impermanence was a function of change; life was change, and everything in it was impermanent. Some things like mountains may outlive us, but they too eventually changed and disappeared.

From an intellectual level, I wasn't sure what to do with the idea of impermanence, and I certainly didn't know how to transform the understanding to an emotional level. I still wanted to control what I could not control. Regarding Carol, I still had difficulty accepting that she had FTD, I still wanted to go back to the life we had before FTD, it still pained me to watch pieces of her personality fall away,

I still felt terrible that my kids had to experience the agony I experienced, and I still grieved these changes. I saw that it was important that we treat everyone and everything as if lent to us, because they are.

I had a nagging sense that my pain could be a conduit to freedom, but how to use it as such was murky and ill defined, like the blurred imagery that lingered in my mind of holy water being poured on my head and into my nose and mouth during baptism and the vague fear I still had about choking on it.

It was like trying to recollect all the features of a person's face and then paint it on a canvass from memory. I could see it and feel it, and I thought I could pick up a paintbrush and have my mind automatically fill the gaps, but my finished painting always proved differently. I decided to read more about impermanence.

Rain, Rain, Go Away

On a late spring day, I looked out my window, and the skies were a mass of tall, thick, clouds swollen with gloom, threatening to release rain in sheets over our area. Thunder rumbled like the low warning growl of a dog that felt you were invading its territory. There was no question about getting a drenching; I just hadn't realized the extent of it.

Carol was sitting on the couch in our first-floor family room, watching TV, which was part of our routine when she was finished with breakfast. I was in the next room as the downpour commenced, but I thought I heard gently pattering drops falling in the family room. I asked Carol if everything was all right, and she responded, "Yes."

I wasn't convinced, so I stuck my head around the doorjamb of the adjoining room and saw fat droplets dripping from the ceiling. The floor was becoming saturated, and the droplets were falling on the couch next to her, but she made no effort to get out of the way. As it turned out, the plumbing had backed up, and the water sought its own level directly over her. Whether she remained on the couch due to lack of judgment or lack of interest, both symptoms of FTD, I couldn't say, but it was one more sad revelation of the degree of her mental degeneration.

FTD presents itself in many forms including repetitive compulsive behaviors such as tapping, clapping, or smacking the lips. Carol clapped throughout most of the day. It was difficult for most people to endure when visiting us, including our children. Tori was working for me in my home-based business, and the continuous rhythmic applause made her crazy, as it would anyone trying to concentrate or relax. There was no refuge from the intrusive sound.

Fortunately, I was able to hear the incessant noise as joyful music that came from a person who was happy. Carol didn't clap aimlessly. She did it as if it was synchronized with the beat of the music she heard in her head. There was enthusiasm and a force that made her body bounce joyously. Her face filled with delight and all the pride that comes with self-accomplishment. Her clapping signaled to me that she was happy and felt safe despite having a disease. I could not fully appreciate the impact on her, since I couldn't know what was happening in her mind. To me, her enthusiastic clapping and cheery face revealed contentment. This proved to me she wasn't in physical pain or mental distress, and that provided great comfort.

Carol would find humor in things that weren't remotely funny, letting out giggles at inappropriate moments or with tragic subject matter. This too made for its own humor in that it functioned as comic relief from the tension of whatever drama we confronted in the privacy of our home or under public scrutiny.

Her preference for sweets and carbohydrates made it difficult to manage her weight, and she couldn't exercise vigorously. Her daily walks weren't enough to burn calories, and she still paused every ten feet to clap before moving on. I was still hiding food so that she wouldn't impulsively eat it.

It's Hard to Swallow

I had to be careful about the foods I served Carol, since there was always a danger of choking or food going into the lungs instead of the stomach, which could lead to pneumonia.

I made certain to serve foods that were soft and cut into bite-sized pieces. I turned off the TV when we were eating so that she wouldn't become distracted, added sauce to keep food moist, made sure she drank fluids during the meal, was careful about bones, helped her pace her eating, and made sure she remained upright after eating so that the food went down properly.

Before I give the wrong impression that I was a cooking aficionado, I'll proclaim that I'd rather gallop to hell on a racehorse than be held hostage by a kitchen. I knew Carol liked eggplant parmesan, crab cakes, pasta, salmon, and a few other meals that were the staples of a nearby specialty store, so I relied on my talent for using an oven to heat and serve. Neither of us complained.

At this time, Dr. Devi told me that if Carol's ability to swallow food was compromised, she may need to rely on a feeding tube. Although her comment was strictly informational, I struggled with the idea. The entire journey was a struggle against the progression of FTD. Just as I began to accept a symptom, a new one appeared and stabbed at the tenderness of my grief.

Caregivers, Angels of Mercy

Dr. Devi had been encouraging me to hire a caregiver for three years. Knowing that I hadn't embraced the idea, she suggested that I use someone part time if only for my own well-being. The recommendation finally resonated with me.

I went on social websites, searching out offers for part-time caregivers, and created my own ad but wasn't successful. I tried an online marketplace where families could find professionals who provided caregiving services. The one I made use of was divided into two parts: one for people like me seeking caregivers and one for caregivers seeking people who needed care. The website let users explore the different caregiving profiles based on individual needs.

I posted an ad, seeking someone to help two hours per day. They would wake Carol, bathe her, make her breakfast, give her morning medications, and take her for a short walk. Carol didn't need a nurse or a certified professional, just assistance with personal care and companionship while I worked. Since caring for someone with FTD came with unique challenges and requirements, I wanted a person with experience in this area. The caregiver would need to be able to adapt to worsening symptoms such as loss of thinking and conversation, increased disorientation, difficulty swallowing, inability to understand the passing of time or recognize people, and inability care for themselves in daily activities. I put together a list of interview questions that took these aspects into consideration.

The progressive aspect of FTD is unique to each individual, so the services and challenges that caregivers faced could be far reaching. It was a trying ordeal that I learned on my own over the years.

There were intangibles that I factored into my search, like making sure the caregiver was alert so that they could plan and be aware of safety needs. They should be able to assess situations, make judgment calls about behavior, and notice subtle safety hazards. A particular concern with Carol was that she would often pick up an item and try to eat it whether it was a petal from a flower that had fallen on a table or inedible things that were small enough to put into her mouth.

Carol was still sociable and enjoyed having company, so social engagement and making sure her emotional needs were met were important parts of caring for her. Of course, honesty and integrity were critical when one human being was dependent on another for their existence. Though all the key qualities I listed were important, the one that I could not compromise on was compassion, and it was difficult to assess whether a person had it without knowing them personally.

A loving heart that endeavors to improve another's quality of life by caring for them is perhaps the most essential attribute of a caregiver. The compassion to care for those who cannot care for themselves is the essence of humanness. Compassion provides the ability to maintain patience and empathy when faced with the day-to-day frustrations of caring for an FTD patient with symptoms like restlessness, clapping, tapping, roaming, and when they don't respond well to direction or impulsively do things they shouldn't. Compassion demands that a caregiver not feel annoyed or resentful, be able to take a deep breath, compose themselves, and refocus on the big picture.

Compassion provides for dignity that a person deserves when helping them dress, applying makeup, using the bathroom, fixing their hair, or washing in the shower. It is the thoughtfulness needed to notice subtle changes in mental and physical states or making sure they don't open a door and wander off. It is needed for communication that's done in a kind manner with relaxed body language and a supportive tone. It's also needed to forgive ourselves for lapses and the determination to do better in the future.

I wanted the caregiver to be involved in most aspects of Carol's care. Since I lived and worked in our home, I was able to oversee a caregiver's performance in all these areas. Although I was only looking for two hours per day, I knew at some point I would need the hours extended, so my plan was to find someone who could accommodate this schedule. I knew that the chance of finding someone who met all my requirements was nearly impossible since Mother Theresa was no longer with us. I would have to compromise on some requirements, but I wasn't going to concede any of them upfront.

I interviewed several candidates by phone and met with the person I felt was the best fit.

Give Me Attitude

People who have grown up in metropolitan New York City have an ear for the differences in dialect, word usage, and attitude that indicate what borough they're from or whether they come from north or central New Jersey. When I introduced myself as Anthony to the caregiver I was about to interview, she said, "Maryann." The accent and attitude that went into saying her name told me she was from Staten Island. A metro New York attitude is something you acquire growing up in the area, and it can't be learned later in life. It is not a subtle distinction.

It is as if New Yorkers wear their exposure to roaring trucks, squeaking brakes, car horns, road congestion, and the whining roar of low-flying jets like a loud suit. Ironically, these are the same agitations that lull New Yorkers to sleep at night.

Metro New Yorkers think fast on their feet. It's like we make twenty more decisions per day and do it ten times faster than the rest of the world, and all this energy gives speed and force to the words that come from our mouths. There are subtle distinctions that separate people from Bronx, Brooklyn, Queens, Manhattan, Staten Island, and parts of New Jersey.

I was too focused on the interview to try to decipher them, so I asked Maryann directly where she was from. She belted out, "Staten Island," but it sounded like "Statniland." I knew immediately she was telling the truth, as only people from Staten Island pronounced it like she did, as one word. I'd noticed that Staten Islanders were warm-hearted. They could appear standoffish, but when they learned you were ill, they'd drop off a casserole or drive to the pharmacy for you. They were dependable, offered safe harbor in a storm, and generally cared about the common good.

I admit my assessment was born of prejudice, but I found these traits to be true of Maryann. Importantly, she also had managerial experience in the caregiving industry and had worked firsthand with dementia patients. I hired her.

Having someone care for Carol wasn't what I wanted, but Dr. Devi convinced me that having a few hours to run errands, have lunch with a friend, or hit golf balls at the driving range would be therapeutic. I was still working, so paying a caregiver for two hours per weekday wasn't a financial burden.

From Zero to Zen

The first time I got into the car to do a chore without Carol—and with Maryann as caregiver—was difficult. It was a milestone in that it was a sad reminder we were no longer inseparable, that our time together could no longer be assumed. I was starting a new chapter after nearly forty years of loving her. It was one more sense of loss added to all the others I had experienced.

I also felt enormous guilt. Carol was my partner, and I felt I was cheating on her by not including her in my moment of freedom. I could see it was easier to feel guilty about taking a break from caregiving than wanting to fight it. I tried not to let sadness and guilt distract me, but it would take many car rides before I began to accept the empty passenger seat and many radio station changes to avoid hearing the songs that reminded me of better times.

One day as I was driving, and I felt the emptiness of not having my wife next to me. I was reminded about impermanence being a function of life, that life was change. It struck me that my misery was being caused by not accepting the temporariness of life. This idea inspired me to look again for a disciplined practice that made use of my experience and helped transform grief into something positive, a higher awareness that might help me cope with grieving.

My search brought me to articles on Zen Buddhism, and the spiritual concepts resonated with me. They provided insight into grief, and I saw it could provide a path toward comfort and help me understand the truth of existence. I don't claim to be Buddhist, certainly not in the traditional sense, but I wanted to pursue an understanding of impermanence, which was a keystone of Buddhism. I had been striving for permanence in life whether it was a favorite car, good health, holding on to youth, keeping close relationships with friends, or wishing good times would stay forever and tough times never reappeared.

Buddhism teaches that all things—good and bad, joy and sorrow, material and ideological, mountain and river—are temporary. Some things may outlive us, but their demise is inescapable over time. Impermanence is fundamental to life, and life has no recognition of stability for stability's sake. Because we have attachments to things we like or want, when they change or we lose them, we experience grief. We suffer when we experience something we *don't* like or want and when we *do* want things to change but life won't change them to the way we want. Our failure to willingly live the unchangeable circumstances of our lives causes grief. It is the root of suffering.

Grief or suffering work on a deeper level than is usually obvious. When things are the way we want them, we want to *believe* they will always be this way. When life is good, we want to *believe* it will always be good or suppose it *should* always be good. We emphasize the future and ask ourselves how we can maintain or increase the goodness whether it has to do with making money, holding on to happiness, getting a promotion, or realizing our dreams.

As well, *believing* that when things in our lives don't go the way we want when we can't maintain or increase the good things, when we lose money, become unhappy, don't get the promotion, or don't realize our dreams causes us to lose sight of the future and *believe* that life should be different from what it is, but life is life. It is not personal. It goes about doing what life does, and life is not good, bad, or ugly; it simply *is*. Our interpretation makes it feel good, bad, or ugly, but *our willingness* to live it the way it is given to us (if we can't change it) lessens our grief and suffering, perhaps even to the point of eliminating it.

As someone who felt significant loss as pieces of Carol were chipped away, the idea of impermanence seemed important. Though I was able to glean an intellectual understanding of the causes of grief and suffering, I had no idea how to make use of it to cope or grow in awareness. Grief felt permanent. It had settled in and felt endless.

Carol's FTD, caring for her, and working on my business continued to stress me. Underneath the stress I sensed anxiety, nervousness, and fear. The anxiety was mental, emotional, and physical, impacted the way I thought, and made me oversensitive to body sensations. An ache or pain that I might not normally pay attention to became a worry, almost a rumination.

The stress, grief, and anxiety had me concerned that the collective impact would trigger depression, panic disorder, and agoraphobia. I logically understood that my ignorance of impermanence and desire to control change were the root of all my torments. My thoughts were like clouds that hid the sun.

I ordered a few books on Zen Buddhism in a search for answers. I found some of the books written by Zen masters to be hefty reading—it was as if you had to have an in-depth knowledge of Zen to understand what the author was discussing. I understood the words but not the context in which they were used. Other books were too long, notoriously difficult to read, or blindingly brilliant with prose. In the end, they all fell short of showing me a simple method of practice. I wasn't sure where to turn next but wasn't giving up. I got just enough understanding from the books to feel that I was headed in the right direction.

THE YEAR 2021
(SECOND HALF)

Odds and Ends

I began giving Carol a blend of organic food in a squeez-able pouch in the afternoons as a treat—not because she couldn't eat solid food but because I knew the pouch was straightforward for her to handle, and the pureed contents were easy for her to swallow. One day, she was about to brush her teeth, and instead of putting the toothpaste on the brush, she put the tip of the tube into her mouth and was about to squeeze. I reached for it and gently took it away. I'm not sure if the toothpaste tube reminded her of the food pouch, but it was another revelation of FTD progression.

Carol's birthday was nearing, and I asked her to tell me the date. I asked easy questions at times and used them as a test of the FTD progress. I could see she was struggling to remember the date, so I changed the subject.

On a cool September day, I was driving her to a dental appointment and was wondering how the teeth cleaning would go. I knew she had dental anxiety and used to ask for laughing gas to keep her calm, but now the sedative wasn't recommended because of the FTD. She never told me the reason for her nervousness, but I supposed it was the same for most of us: the sterile smell of the room, the drilling sounds in the background, a hygienist up close and personal while sticking an instrument in our mouth, or feeling self-conscious about sitting in a dentist's chair with mouth wide open and unable to see what's happening.

Given the challenge we had getting her into positions for a breast exam, I was sure that following directions from a dentist to bite down, open her mouth, and position the tongue to allow for the dental vacuum and other equipment might be problematic, and it was. Fortunately, they were able to do an excellent job of cleaning her teeth, but taking x-rays presented a problem. Each time the dentist tried to put the x-ray film and equipment in her mouth, Carol instinctively used her tongue to keep it from entering. It was a natural reflex to having a bulky, uncomfortable, foreign object put in her mouth. The more the dentist tried to maneuver around her tongue, the more Carol used it to push it out.

I could see that the hygienist and dentist hadn't worked with a neurologically impaired patient before, and an anxious atmosphere surrounded the procedure, but there was a genuine interest in using it as an opportunity to broaden their knowledge of patient challenges. At our future visits, I was thankful for the significant strides they had made.

Buttons, Impermanence, and Lights Out

I'd lay Carol's clothes on the bed, and she would dress herself. I had been doing this for some time since she wasn't able to pick out the outfits to wear. It was an unseasonably hot day, and I picked out summer clothes and went about straightening up our bedroom. As I reached for a pair of socks to put in the hamper, I noticed that she had put on her sandals before her jeans. She was staring at them with a confused look as if trying to figure out how she could put on jeans while wearing sandals. After this, helping her dress became part of our routine.

She started turning off lights when I was in the middle of doing something and needed light to see. It would normally be the perfect opportunity to unleash my characteristic impatience, but I couldn't begin to get annoyed with her, because her innocence, happy attitude, and dainty cuteness neutralized any irritation.

I was cooking our dinner one evening—well, more accurately, I was heating it up in the microwave—and didn't realize I had left a bag of candy on the kitchen counter. I heard munching and knew Carol had found it and the contents would be devoured. As I turned to put the candy away, I heard a terribly loud crunch and couldn't imagine what had made the sound. I spun around, saw her chewing, and heard another loud crunch. I rushed over and asked her to open her mouth. I found she was grinding on a coat button the size of a nickel. Fortunately, she didn't break any teeth or swallow it.

These changes in her thinking and behavior had me thinking about how they might be problematic. I tried to plan and prepare for every situation. I knew about the symptoms that could be expected and the outcomes of conditions, so ensuring her safety was a priority. I developed a skill for assessing situations and noticing subtle changes in behavior and symptoms and made lists of them so I could relay them to Dr. Devi on our visits.

I was Carol's emotional support and always doing silly things to get her to laugh. I was responsible for her happiness and keeping her at ease. I participated in almost all her care and was the connection between medical professionals and her family. I was making judgment calls on most issues related to her health and best interests. At times, the demands were overwhelming. There were times at the day's end that I just wanted to sit in front of the TV, escape the care and work burdens, and be fully absorbed in a movie. Carol would begin clapping or become restless. Symptoms changed instantly, which was emotionally straining. People told me that I had to take care of myself, which was an insightful suggestion, but I secretly wished they'd complete the idea by suggesting a way to do it.

I kept thinking about the impermanence of things in my life and the fast pace at which everything was changing. I was processing life as though I resented it for making the things that were important to me temporary. I faced a choice: I could continue my tantrum and refuse to let go of what I thought life should be, or I could accept that my relationship with Carol was fundamentally changed and would forever be changing and be willing to live life as it was presented.

It seemed like an abstract approach to dealing with grief, but it made a shift in the way I viewed it. I could see that fighting impermanence was the cause of my grief, suffering, and anxiety. I became aware that at one point during the day, my suffering might feel endless, but at another point, it was gone. This didn't necessarily change the hurt I felt in the moment, but it did change my perspective.

Don't Get Attached

Along with impermanence, another precept important to understanding the root cause of our suffering in Zen Buddhism is attachment. We lead our lives trying to clutch, or cling to, people and things we believe will make us happy and avoid the things that we don't. Our attachment is a source of suffering, because the things we cling to are momentary, impermanent, and changing, and therefore they provide only temporary satisfaction.

If attaching ourselves to people and things brings us anxiety and suffering when we lose them, nonattachment must be a remedy. If attachment leads to an unsatisfactory life, nonattachment is helpful for a satisfactory life. Nonattachment doesn't mean that we give up the people and things we want in our lives. It is acknowledging that they, like us, are impermanent.

An important distinction is that nonattachment is not the same as *detachment*. I don't want to detach from the people and things I want in my life, but life has its own way of unfolding. It is separate from my impossible attempts to control it. Nonattachment is what happens when I let go of the *need* to be in control of what is occurring and allow the present moment to be what it only can be. It is being present in the moment given to us without fixating on the moment as being better or worse. Nonattachment is the awareness that comes with understanding the futility of trying to control life.

I explored Zen Buddhism and a practice called mindful meditation as an extension of my interest in impermanence. From my understanding, there are slight but crucial differences between Zen Buddhism and mindful meditation.

Mindful meditation is a training practice that helps us slow racing thoughts, let go of negativity, and calm the mind and body. It involves being fully focused on "the now" so we can acknowledge and accept our thoughts, feelings, and sensations without judgment. For me, calming the mind and body through mindful meditation is temporary. It doesn't last as I encounter stresses throughout the day, because it doesn't address the source of my anxieties and suffering: the *self*.

Zen Buddhism addresses the self. It equates the self to an egotistical state that must be transcended in order to experience unity with nature and divine consciousness.

Don't Be Selfish

Zen Buddhism views self as "lesser self" and "greater self." The "lesser self" is our ego, which is easily influenced by situations and desires and affected by impermanence and change: the cause of suffering. In comparison, practicing Zen Buddhism awakens the "greater self" to the interconnectedness of life and all that sustains us. This withers the lesser self and therefore suffering opens us to our natural state of compassion.

Zen Buddhism and mindful meditation helped me understand that the past I wanted so badly, the past I was attached to, and the life I wanted with Carol exists only in my mind. The past is neurons firing in my brain. It is not real. It is the same for the future—it does not exist except as my mind imagines it, whether I am anticipating worrisome outcomes or speculating on fantasies I want to become real. The only real thing that exists is each moment of life.

I began to appreciate that if I was anyplace other than each moment, thinking about the past or future, worrying about something that may or may not happen, ruminating about an argument with someone earlier in the day, or thinking about the jerk who cut me off on the highway one hour earlier, I was not living my life. I was mentally someplace other than the moment in a place that wasn't real since I was focusing on a past or future that did not exist. I couldn't be centered on past or future thoughts and living life at the same time. If I was absorbed in my imagination, I robbed myself of living life.

Life Is Our Instructor

We are a culture that relies on specialists to fix problems in our lives. People come to us as experts or we go to them, but I think we have an awareness of ourselves. We can develop the confidence that allows us to find a means to cope with the things that upset or confuse us or that we find unlikable. We don't need someone else to tell us what to do, as on some level, we know that we are the only person who knows what is right for us.

We don't need an expert to free us from the anxieties that are caused by life, though we may need someone who can guide us in learning ways to practice. It's not *life* that torments us; it's the way we respond to it. In this way, life is our instructor, our expert. It gives us everything we need, and we just need a way to understand how to learn from it.

We are the center of our life though it may not look nice. Life may be illness, aging, loss of a loved one or something we value, or confronting our mortality. None of us wants to face these things, and we don't want them in our lives, but our suffering is caused by our unwillingness to experience the powerful feelings that come with them. We create ways to avoid or refuse to accept them, or we remain in shock because our ignorance keeps us from considering their possibilities or accepting them as they happen.

Practicing Meditation

At this point, I'd been practicing meditation for eight months. After gleaning the information on Zen Buddhism and mindful meditation, I put together a way to meditate that I thought was a powerful tool for managing my grief and anxiety. None of the concepts were mine; I simply put them in a form that was easy to understand and use. The important thing about meditation was that it took practice to learn to be present, to tolerate and be willing to engage grief as well as other emotions. Practicing meditation was helping me understand that the grief I had with Carol's FTD, or any grief, was a natural part of my life.

When I practice meditation, I focus on my breathing, slowly attuning to the sensation of air moving in my body. I feel my diaphragm rise and fall as the air enters and leaves my nostrils. The focus on breathing takes my attention from my thoughts and allows them to slow so I can step back and witness the drama in my mind (like the first time Carol forgot to take her handbag with her; I knew it was a significate sign of the progressing FTD, and this thought created sorrow, worry, and deep pain over the loss of a part of her).

Then I witness my thoughts without judgment. *Carol has forgotten her handbag. This has never happened before and is a sign the FTD is worsening.* I acknowledge the thought. I may silently repeat it, and it begins to fade and disappear. As I continue to do this with the thoughts that arise, my mind begins to quiet. I can witness the emotions and body sensations I'm feeling, which is heavy sadness in my heart and the fear I feel in my stomach. I witness where these sensations are located and allow myself to experience them. As I experience the sensations, they too begin to diminish and quiet, and I am left with an awareness of the reality.

Living with FTD is my life and Carol's life, and the only healthy option I have is to experience life as it is. This awareness did not come during my first meditation session but through months of practicing meditation, witnessing the thoughts and body sensations as they happened.

Witnessing shows me I am separate from my thoughts, separate from my body sensations, and an awareness grows that I am living what is my life, not living the thoughts swirling in my mind. Trying to live what I want life to be and not what life is causes my suffering. Dedication to practicing meditation increases this awareness. In my experience, there are phases of transformation that take place over months and years.

The worrisome thoughts and emotional and physical pain I have about the progression of FTD do nothing to change the reality of FTD, and the anxiety and deep sadness I have negatively affect my mental and physical health.

It took eight months of practicing this method daily before I admitted that my life *is* caring for Carol. The circumstances of my life have changed and can be no different than what they are. Yes, I have options I can consider about Carol's care, but caring for her in our home is the only option that comes from an understanding of my true self, the greater self.

Engaging strong emotions straightforwardly can be challenging, especially in the beginning stages of practicing meditation, but by doing so, I find that the grief isn't so terrible and overwhelming as it was at first. There is nothing wrong with me, no error in me to uncover. Grief is an opportunity, like a coach or trainer, to be used to recognize the impact it is having on my thoughts and body sensations. Recognizing the impact of grief raises my awareness, and the result is a diminishing of grief. I'm finding this to be true for all emotions.

As I become less *self*-centered, or as grief and other emotions diminish, there is more room to care about someone else without expecting anything in return. I am finding that as my ego shrinks, it is replaced with compassion. I begin to see life as it is.

Regarding Carol's FTD, practicing meditation is a way for me to face the powerful emotions that come with the realities of aging, illness, losing the things I love about her, and the reality of my mortality. There is an important distinction between *knowing* that Carol has FTD and I must care for her and being *aware* of it.

Knowing means I go through the motions of doing what is necessary but with a mindset that I don't want to believe it or be made to endure such an injustice. It is using my time trying to construct a life in my mind that isn't true. It's a form of resisting reality, and resistance manifests in emotions like depression, denial, anger, frustration, and anxiety. Resistance is a hollow hope that someone will change my situation or ease some of the burden.

No one can change my situation, experience it for me, serve my time, or live my life but me. By growing this *awareness* through meditation, I see more clearly that I have no hope of changing that which cannot be changed. It is my situation, my pain, or my joy, but the point is that I must own it.

Being free is losing the false hope that I can control or change that which cannot be controlled. Being free is doing what is there for me to do and not trying to imagine it differently. Being present in the moment is having no need for anything else. This applies not only to dealing with FTD or its symptoms throughout the day. It is also being free to be present when cleaning the house, taking out the trash, picking up after the dogs, or dealing with an irate customer. It is the freedom to be the circumstances of my life. This is

Anthony P. Mauro Sr.

starting to bring moments of joy, because I am not fulfilling what I want for myself but fulfilling the needs of life before me. I am not avoiding suffering but *being* my suffering.

At this point, I had glimpses of the awareness described. It was still unrefined, more of a notion, but enough for me to want to pursue more, because I could see the potential for growth. By practicing meditation, I was starting to understand that caring for Carol could be an extension of caring for me. They weren't separate.

On the Right Track

I am heading down the trail of my life, and a higher awareness is illuminating the way, but it is an undertaking. It is a commitment, and I need to practice meditation every time thoughts and emotions arise. Sometimes, it is painful. In the beginning, there were times that the emotions were so strong that I couldn't confront them, but I'd revisit them later or the next day. I'd experienced progress some days only to feel like I was back at the starting point the next day.

Practicing meditation is hard. To be effective, it takes the dedication of a professional. It takes discipline, persistence, patience, and determination. It reminds me of when I started playing golf years ago. I took a few lessons from a pro at a local course, and he told me I first needed to learn the essential skill of a golf swing. He said that skill development demanded focused repetition that became a habit. Repetition increased confidence, provided feedback, and would allow me to build proficiency with a golf swing. Skill development took time and patience, because improvement was never linear.

Practicing meditation with strong emotions can be uncomfortable and tedious. Like learning a golf swing, one day I'd feel as if I was mastering it because I saw good results, but the next day or days later, my shots seemed worse than when I started, and I'd question whether I should abandon the effort.

Skill development in meditation can be long and require patience, and knowing this can help ease excessive expectations. There is no perfection except if perfection is defined as the thoughts and body sensations we experience at any moment and using them as fodder for meditation.

I practice meditation when I'm angry because someone is rude to me, when I resent getting a phone call at an inopportune time, when my dog eats something that makes him sick and ends it up on the carpet, or when someone monopolizes a conversation with an ego so large it feels as if it sucks the air from the room.

It is apparent to me that not practicing meditation takes a toll that is greater than the effort of practicing. There is no freedom, joy, and compassion in refusing to practice, but these are the outcomes of practice. Over time, I build trust in the process and feel assured things will work out as well as they can with circumstances as they are.

It seems like a contradiction that learning to tolerate and be willing to be present with grief is the way to diminish it, but it does. It helps me to understand that FTD grief, and all grief, is a part of my life. It's challenging at times, but in and of itself, it is not so terrible once I become accustomed to it. It means I love Carol.

Grief is impermanent. There is nothing to answer, nothing to repair, and nothing to do with the grief itself except to recognize its impact on me.

I practice meditation in the morning because I find my mind is calmest at that time, before stresses accumulate and demands begin. There are some mornings when I don't have strong or painful emotions, and on these days, I try to expand my awareness by practicing with the emotions that come from addressing life's stark realities.

From books and articles, I learned that Buddha criss-crossed northern India giving a wealth of profound teachings, and underlying them all were Four Nobel Truths, the cornerstone of Zen Buddhism: 1. There is suffering. 2. There is a cause of suffering. 3. There is an end to suffering. 4. There is a way to free ourselves from suffering called the eightfold path (Buddha's practical instructions to end suffering).

One kind of suffering is the physical and mental distress caused by illness, old age, and death. Another kind is the distress we experience from the impermanent nature of life and change. There is the pain we feel when we lose things that we value and people we love. I created a list of these stark realities that cause us suffering so I could incorporate them into practicing meditation. I call them The Six Realities.

The Six Realities
That Cause Us Suffering Due to Attachments

1. We all die

2. We all experience illness

3. We all age

4. We all lose things we love

5. We all lose people we love

6. Every second of life is change

I incorporate The Six Realities into my meditation. On days when my thoughts and emotions are already calm, I think of the first cause of suffering from the list, *We all die*. I pause to witness and acknowledge any thoughts and body sensations it arouses. If the thoughts continue, I again witness the thought and acknowledge it. When I think, *We all die,* it may bring the thought, *I don't want to die.* I witness this thought and acknowledge it. I also witness the body sensations that go with it, which might be nervousness in my upper chest, pain in my stomach, or my heart beating rapidly.

I then think of the next reality, *We all experience illness*. I pause to witness and acknowledge the thoughts and body sensations that arise from it. When I think, "*We all experience illness*," it may bring a thought such as "*Someday I might get cancer.*" I witness this thought, acknowledge it, and experience the body sensation that goes with it, which might be the strong fear I feel in my upper stomach. If I experience the fear in my upper stomach, I let it be. I don't try to deny, suppress, or distract myself from it.

I use this meditative practice with each of The Six Realities. They may or may not apply at a particular moment, but they are all eventual, and this by itself provokes thoughts and strong feelings. This is useful practice, because as I witness and allow myself to experience them, I begin to see they are an integral part of life and that I have been dismissive of them, especially when I was young and my attention was elsewhere. I would think, *They only happen to other people.*

Practicing meditation with The Six Realities engages us in life's toughest punches. We expand our ability to cope, because we see they will happen to us or touch us. We put more value on the people and time we have in our lives instead of obsessing with the thoughts that aren't real. We begin to live in each moment, which is real. As I do this, emotionally *self*-centered thoughts recede, and *life*-centered thoughts broaden. I become wiser, solutions to my problems become clearer, and I become more compassionate.

Practicing this type of meditation is not easy. Sometimes I'm uncomfortable dealing with strong emotions. It can be painful, daily meditation can get boring, or I can go weeks or months without seeing progress, but the practice helps to shed light on my ruminations as being unreal.

If I don't practice with my worries, I find they agitate me, and as I ruminate with them over time, they make me physically sick, anxious, and depressed. By practicing meditation, I become more familiar with myself and how my life works. I'm given opportunities to peek into my blind spots. I start to see what drives my ego, the patterns in the way I live my life, and my wants. They begin to fade not because I'm trying to make them fade but because the luminosity of awareness causes them to do so.

Importantly, this is a way to address the root of my anxieties and not simply manage the symptoms of panic attacks. I'm getting to know my anxieties and the ways I handle them. The more I practice meditation, the more my anxieties melt. I see that I am managing them based on a history of how I programmed them when I was young. When we're young, we're not equipped to design coping mechanisms with wisdom, so we create convoluted, reactive, and unhealthy ways to survive, and our feelings follow us throughout our lives.

Children want what they want, and when they can't have it, they begin to get the idea that life is difficult. Since they don't know what to do with this dilemma and attribute the cause to themselves, they begin to devise ways to ease the pain and get what they want. Maybe they are cunning enough to respond to the problem by being eager to please, throwing a tantrum, or finding something in between. This becomes the foundation of how they deal with similar circumstances as adults.

Whether the threats we feel are physical ("fight or flight" fear), we unconsciously develop ways to get ourselves out of the situation using the foundation we devised as children. When we feel our circumstance is out of our control, we become frightened, frustrated, or infuriated, and we create a negative belief about ourselves. It is almost impossible to develop healthy coping mechanisms when we are blinded by painful emotions, especially when we're young. Many of us spend a lifetime using strategies we think will work to avoid facing reality or experiencing feelings.

When I practice meditation, I slowly develop the resolve to confront anxiety and pain. This unravels the knots and tangles of the coping mechanisms I devised to avoid suffering, which ironically caused the suffering. As the unreality of my coping mechanisms confronts the realities of life, my awareness of this clash begins to melt unreality, and I start to see my true self, the real me.

Thank God for Bras and Underwear

Maryann had the day off. I finished showering Carol, dried her off, and had her seated in the changing area. I opened the window and felt a genially warm day for November. The sun shone brilliantly, but I had awakened earlier to the warm tingle of a daybreak flush with reds and oranges. The atmosphere was still smoky from the lingering coolness of night meeting the still, stifling air. We'd had a good frost only a few days earlier and, before that, normally cool weather.

I helped her put on incontinence underwear and her bra when my cell phone rang. I saw it was a customer, so I answered. I needed to get a folder from my office to answer a question, which was only a few feet from where we were, so I asked Carol to wait and explained I'd return in a few seconds. My filing system was extremely organized but only to me. To most people, it would look like roadside litter piled up and strewn along the floor, but should any of the disheveled mess be organized to conventional standards, I would never find what I needed.

I found my folder in an instant, but before I returned to Carol, I paused to answer another question my customer had asked, and the explanation kept me in my office longer than expected. I covered the receiver of my phone and called out to Carol that I'd be right back. She didn't answer, so I repeated myself louder.

I turned and looked out the front window of my office, which was perched above our front lawn. My eyes were drawn to movement on the driveway, and as my mind processed what I was seeing, I realized it was Carol taking out the mail, wearing only the bra and incontinence underwear. She found immense pleasure in bringing my office mail out to our mailbox where our postal carrier was kind enough to take it for us. Until that day, she was more than vigilant about doing it fully clothed.

I finished my phone conversation with polite abruptness and rushed to get her. I didn't want to startle her or make her aware that she was flouting our neighborhood's dress code, so I let her finish her mission and walked her back inside. We lived on a quiet cul-de-sac, so no one had seen her, and fortunately it wasn't the hour that the school bus made its rounds. Carol was content with the way she performed her duties and oblivious to the indiscretion. As for me, the event was my initiation to my role as 24-7 watchdog.

I finished getting her dressed and then served breakfast. I noticed that it was taking longer for her to swallow even soft food like scrambled eggs. Midway through chewing, she would stop, seeming to forget that she had food in her mouth. This was a new symptom. However, Dr. Devi had told me that people with FTD could have feeding and swallowing difficulties. They could be messy eaters, have difficulty with some foods and consistencies, there could be coughing and choking, and the symptoms could worsen as FTD progressed. This was something I had to watch closely not only from a caregiver's viewpoint but also as a marker of her cognitive and behavioral decline.

I knew that at some point, a feeding tube might be necessary, and the prospect gnawed at me. My heart was filled with a sadness that felt as heavy as a sandbag, and I thought it would rip from my chest and plunge to my feet. Many of the changes I saw in Carol had a similar effect.

I used my thoughts and body sensations to practice my meditation.

More Practicing

At that time, I witnessed my thoughts, the first being *My heart feels as heavy as a sandbag.* I acknowledged it: *My heart feels as heavy as a sandbag.* The next thought sprang into my mind: *It is too painful to imagine Carol on a feeding tube.* I witnessed the thought and acknowledged it. As more thoughts raced through my mind, I did the same. After a while, I was left with the body sensation of a heavy heart. I witnessed it too and allowed it to be as it was. I didn't fight it or run from it. I wanted to stay with it and feel it. I did this for as long as I could, and after a brief period, my thoughts seemed less frenetic and the burden felt lighter. The heavy sadness was impermanent. It changed, it became lighter, and it left me sooner.

I had been practicing meditation for close to one year at that point. I could clearly recognize when my thoughts caused physical stresses. I was confronting a picture of how I thought my life should be and the tragedy it seemed to be. I was regularly facing tragedy and the drama of my thoughts head on. I was learning about myself.

Just the Way Things Are

It was 4:30 p.m. on an early December day, and I bundled Carol in a heavy coat and scarf for our evening Jeep ride and walk. At this time of year, it got dark early, so I liked to begin while the sun was still hanging in the sky. I drove us to our town's park and chose our regular parking spot close to the trail entrance. I looked through the windshield and noticed the grass had lost its green luster and had the dull, thin look of dormancy. I opened my door and was met by an icy breeze and shivered. My jacket was zipped, but I felt the need to clutch it for a false sense of warmth as I hurried to the passenger side and helped Carol out of the vehicle.

Carol stepped onto the hardened ground, and as I took a long, deep breath, the air stung my lungs like a blast of peppermint. The trees were naked but maintained self-respect, undressed is their winter attire, a way of life that brought no shame. Recurring winds had scattered leaves into predictable piles. The park was silent because the fair-weather visitors had hung up their walking sneakers for the season. It was just Carol and me, as it had been in the past at that time of year. Quiet and cold skies gave the park an eerie quality. A faded and tattered Wet Paint sign clung stubbornly to a bench and fluttered in the breeze, a remnant of the summer past, I supposed. Carol's nose was red from the chill, and mine was leaking.

Carol never turned down a walk whether it was on the hottest of summer days or a frosty one like this one. If the weather was extreme, I suggested that we not walk, and she'd go along with my prompting. For as long as I had known her, she'd had a swift, sure-footed stride, but on this day, she paused every few feet to clap—a symptom, like others, that would occur gradually and progress over time.

Some symptoms hit me harder than others, perhaps because of their severity or my state of mind. Sometimes severity and state of mind collided, as if in a coordinated effort to gang up on me. These were the most painful periods. My ruminations began: *Why is Carol pausing so much? Will this continue? Will this eventually affect her ability to walk?*

My musings continued, and as they did, I felt fear rising. I found these instances the perfect opportunity to practice meditation. Life presents teachable moments, timed for when we need them. As Carol and I walked, I witnessed and acknowledged my racing thoughts and repeated them silently to myself. After a while, I was left with the body sensation of fear. I witnessed it too and allowed it to be. I did it until it started to wither, my thoughts seemed less frenetic, and the burden lightened.

As I practice in the silence that surrounds me in my home, driving in my car, or wherever I am when circumstances cause ruminations and emotions, I begin to have a sense that things will be all right. It isn't that I want things to be the way they are. I still hurt from watching Carol endure FTD and pained by the variables of dealing with it, but there is a growing awareness that I cannot change what life has given both of us. There's a developing understanding that it is useless to fight the inevitable. I am gaining a willingness to let things be as they are. There is love in this understanding, and this love touches Carol and has wonderful effects for her and me. I think this is more evidence that "to every action there is an equal and opposite reaction."

By the end of December, a few more symptoms had emerged. The kidlike wonder and excitement Carol had about going to Burger Brothers dropped away. It was sad to see that something that was enjoyable to her for such a long time had stopped and was never mentioned again.

She wasn't talking as much as she used to. She seemed to understand things that were said to her but did not contribute to a conversation. Most of her responses to questions were yes or no, and even then, I might have to ask her a few times before she answered. Though she still brought the mail out to the mailbox each day, she stopped bringing the mail in, which had been equally important to her. She was becoming distant though she continually displayed a happy demeanor, clapped, loved listening to her music, and sang to songs.

She stopped looking at Find My. She used to open the app, look at the screen, say our names, and announce the town where each of us was located. She had always been protective of her children, and since they had moved from home, she got comfort knowing where they were at any time by using the app. Now, as I put her to bed, I opened the app so she could see the kids' location and read their whereabouts out loud to me.

Taking a Break

Christmas in our home was always filled with laughter, sharing, and recounting memories. This year, we had the kids over on Christmas Eve for our celebration. For Christmas Day, we were invited over to Tori's in-laws, but I was undergoing a spiritual awakening and wanted to spend it with just Carol. It was a day used for reflection, to reconnect, a day of silence from the year's stresses.

I started the morning with Carol opening her gift, made her breakfast, played her favorite Christmas music, and started a Christmas movie marathon. We then went to the park and soaked in the sights, smells, and sounds of Christmas Day. We enjoyed the excitement and added to it by taking a long ride to look at the decorated homes, nativities, Santas, snowmen, and lights exploding with colors that offset the darkness of winter. We were alone but as far from feeling lonely as anyone could be.

THE YEAR 2022

The Year of Caregivers

Progress continued from practicing meditation. Though there were times I felt I had plateaued, feeling plateaued was just where I was at that moment, just a thought for me to witness. The demanding thing about practicing meditation was that I was dealing with the hurt and grief of FTD. I saw Carol 24-7, so each moment was a reminder of the reality we were living and that there was no way to escape it. I was a regular witness to the ravages of the disease. Emotional pain was a normal condition for me, and like most people, I didn't want to deal with it directly.

We arm our suffering by ignoring it and disarm it by embracing it. Meditation can use hurt to stimulate growing awareness, so I have plenty of ammunition and am making progress. The more I practice, the more I can see the nature of life and how I respond to it. This ability continues to get stronger; it takes less effort, and I can do it routinely. I am less consumed by thoughts and can more easily address emotions that arise and see them fade quickly.

Things don't instantly become fixed by practicing meditation. Practice must hobble along, and it can be difficult, baffling, and dispiriting. It takes effort to understand the nature of our experience. The more I do it, the less I am attached to material things I think I need to make me happy, and as a result, I'm becoming happier.

This isn't a magical experience. I'm beginning to know myself better—how I think, the emotional programs I operate from, my body sensations and where they are located—and it is easier to move on to the next thing. I am recognizing suffering in terms of my attachments to things I don't want changed, many of which are part of The Six Realities.

Doctor's Orders

I was sitting in Dr. Devi's office, craning my neck in all directions to look at the degrees, specialties, certificates, and accomplishments that were so omnipresent they virtually functioned as decorative wallpaper. I thought that if an archaeologist unearthed this room at some distant future date and discovered these artifacts, they might place the material remains in historical context by concluding that all human beings of the period were ambitious geniuses or had bizarre tastes in wallpaper.

On many occasions, Dr. Devi had prompted me to get full-time assistance, but it didn't resonate with me. She again suggested I hire a person full time. Maybe it was the gentle tone she used or the look in her eyes, or maybe on that day I was more receptive to advice, but I agreed.

Carol and I were thrifty and had always lived well below our means. This allowed us to save enough so we could travel during our retirement, and we would have done so, but life had other plans. I was still working, so a live-in caregiver was financially manageable. I remained committed to having Carol stay in the comfort of our home for quality-of-life matters.

When I returned home, I called a friend who had suggested a person he used for his mother who had recently passed from Alzheimer's disease. I called her, and she wasn't available, but she did recommend someone named Irina. I interviewed Irina and checked her references. Everything seemed satisfactory.

I knew that someone new living under our roof would change the dynamics of our household, and this was the case with the first candidate I hired, more so than I anticipated.

Irina was of Russian heritage and close to sixty years of age. She was short and stout, and she reminded me of the images I had seen of old Russian women spending their days outside, joining with others to chat on benches in front of their homes. She had a no-nonsense way about her. I imagined it was an aspect she had earned the hard way such as elbowing her way to a seat on a crowded bus or cutting in front of people in a long line at the bank. She never let me forget about the tough times when growing up in Russia. In the summer, she sold fruits, herbs, and vegetables, and in the winter, she jarred jam and tomatoes. She was raised in a small, rural community where the greatest populations of living things were trees. The rare sighting of a bus added life to the lonesome road that bisected the village; the locals called it a road, but she described it as a trodden dirt path marred with potholes.

As a kid, I wondered why people settled in such secluded places hundreds of years ago, and I still wonder to this day. She described a place where untamed nature had once proved victorious and could conquer again. In her settlement, there were several wooden houses with ample space between them, as apparently people living in villages respected their privacy. She had no answer to my question about the futility of living in such a place.

Irina told of summers where the grass grew so fast that it took several days a month to keep it managed and warned of birch trees that could turn abandoned fields into forests within years if left to their own doings. Apparently, animals were everywhere. She described a scene that could have been the artwork of a children's book: dogs barking in protest at a duck sitting on the bank of a pond, kittens huddled under a porch and hiding from the clamor as their mother calmly lapped water from a puddle, and chickens bustling nervously at the center of it all.

It was a region known for growing potatoes, and given that Carol and I were served sweet potatoes practically every day, I surmised it was Irina's preferred variety. These orange tubers became a "second bread" for us. She dished them out mashed, baked, fried, and featured in everything from casseroles to salads. By the end of her first week, I had eaten so many sweet potatoes that I couldn't stand the thought of them. The taste of what was once the highlight of fall and winter for me had been exploited to the point of dislike. It was like killing my favorite song by being made to listen to it over and over until I couldn't stand to hear it one more time. The sweet potato had become dead to me.

There were other uneasy issues with our living arrangement. I didn't know if they were the habits, rituals, practices, lifestyles, or traditions of culture, but the house was left unkempt. Food was splattered all over the microwave, crumbs were left across the counter, and moldy food was kept in the refrigerator (yes, mostly sweet potatoes). I saw a film of grease around the stove. The stench of cigarette smoke emanated from her bedroom. She didn't tell me she smoked until after I hired her, and though we agreed it was to be done outside the home, apparently her commitment was made in calculation and not sincerity.

These were other annoyances, nothing that would make me terminate her services, but there were performance issues too. One of Irina's primary responsibilities was to make sure that Carol went for a walk twice a day if the weather permitted. I learned that she had a bad hip and couldn't keep up with Carol's pace. She was out of shape and constantly stopping to catch her breath as Carol marched onward, so monitoring was not done satisfactorily. Her problem hip also made it cumbersome for her to properly help Carol with bathing and dressing.

I had three conversations with Irina about the need to improve areas of care and performance, but there was no improvement in any of them. I felt bad about letting her go, and I didn't want to hurt her feelings or dignity. My primary concern was that Carol wasn't getting the level of care required, and unfortunately the necessity for change can make short shrift of a tough task.

I practiced meditation on my thoughts and the body sensations they caused before having a conversation with her. I found that the know-how from practice provided an awareness of what I wanted out of a circumstance and the ability to act from it. Practicing meditation didn't change the fact it was best to terminate her. It gave me more clarity that it must be done and made me softer, respectful, unpretentious, empathetic, and compassionate in my approach to delivering what I understood to be hurtful news. I gave Irina two weeks' notice. The approach made living together for two more weeks easier for both of us.

Me, a Human Resource Manager

I felt that hiring caregivers was like taking on the talent acquisition trends and adversities of a Fortune 500 company. I was beginning to think I was a full-time human resource manager, and sarcastically thought I might need to use virtual recruiting technologies and promise candidates personal growth and development of new skills in order to hire them.

Dr. Devi was able to recommend someone, and the next hire went smoothly. Tina was originally from Georgia. I didn't know much about the country but was soon to be given encyclopedic knowledge. Georgia is on the southern slopes of the Caucasus Mountains, forming a natural border with the North Caucasian republics of the Russian Federation. The country stretches along the Greater Caucasus ridge and is bordered by the Black Sea to the west, the Armenian and Turkish highlands to the south, and Azerbaijan to the east.

Our new angel of mercy, which I found was a synonym for a compassionate caregiver, was from Tbilisi, the capital of Georgia. From the Mongol to the Soviet, numerous empires left their mark on the capital, which sits on the wandering Mtkvari River. If the food Tina cooked was any reflection on the culture, it was one that demanded everything be fresh, natural, bought locally, bursting with flavor, and displayed artistically. She showed me pictures of her country: magical settings, mountaintop monasteries, leafy valleys, vineyards, winding roads, and dramatic demonstrations of nature's colors.

Tina was a thirty-six-year-old with a long slender frame, ample independence, a streak of regality, and an unusual ability to transform into surliness if I accidentally tripped over one of her unknowable triggers. On one occasion, I returned a jar of almond butter to the cabinet and turned to see her icy glare, scrunched nose, brows snapped together, and lips squeezed so thinly they were drained of color.

I asked with a sense of confusion, "What?"

I'm not sure how she managed to navigate the ten feet that separated us in a single bound, but she elbowed me aside and illustrated that I had not placed the jar "label forward," a task she had just completed doing with every item on all three levels of cabinet shelving. I took a step back and noticed that each item was aligned in perfect rows and columns with the labels facing forward. I never made that mistake again unless it was my mischievous attempt to provoke her, which I admit could give me pleasure at appropriate moments.

I became acquainted with other eccentricities. One time, I didn't realize she was between loads of washing her clothing and tossed mine into the empty washing machine. I received a clipped lecture on how she had spent an hour cleaning dog hair from the washer only to now have my clothes adulterate the machine with the dog hair on them. I'm not sure there was any dog hair, but I vowed never to make that mistake again unless mischief got the better of me.

Putting these harmless and quirky moments aside, and plenty more I encountered, Tina did an excellent job of caring for Carol, and that was my primary concern. She was attentive and communicated with patience, understanding, and empathy. She played Carol's favorite music on walks and showed her family photos to stimulate memories. I admit to the irony of me paying her compliments for being meticulous. She prepared meals, did light housekeeping, gave medication, helped with groceries and clothes shopping, and assisted in taking Carol to medical appointments. Fortunately, Carol didn't need a high level of nursing care, but direct experience with dementia was important, and Tina had some.

More Anecdotes

In February, there were more signs of the FTD progressing. They were painful, and I incorporated witnessing and acknowledging my thoughts and body sensations into my meditation. Carol no longer sat up on her own when getting out of bed. I needed to encourage her and assist by taking her hands and gently pulling her upright. Once she was standing, I noticed that her walk was less steady and lacked confidence.

I also noticed that her legs hung partially over the bed and out from under the covers, so I watched for this and placed them securely on the mattress. She slept on one side and never tossed or turned throughout the night, so I rubbed her legs, back, and shoulders in the morning to stimulate blood circulation.

I began my day at 5:00 a.m. out of habit, not necessity. I found that waking at that hour, earlier than most others, gave me a head start for my day. It created a good feeling that I had found motivating for forty years. It was proactive and forward thinking. It was a form of self-mastery, and it made me feel like I had a hold over my daily activities. I was more organized and disciplined. On the other hand, maybe I did it because I knew no better way. If there is one thing I know, it is that I don't know as much as I think I know. At 5:00 a.m., I saw the world wake up before me. The sky was dark, it was quiet, and few people were moving about.

It was as if the world had stopped and there was goodwill for a sunrise that brought a new beginning, a new day to learn and things to appreciate. I could observe nature and people coming to life. It added a magical quality to each day. I used the time to have a relaxed breakfast, meditate, and exercise before I started work.

I always checked on Carol when I woke. I got up and went to her side of the bed to make sure she was fully under the covers. I plugged her iPhone into the charger, and if she opened her eyes, which was normally the case, I kissed her good morning. She would fall back to sleep. My routine was to let her sleep until 10:00 a.m. Today was no different. At 10:00 a.m., I went into our bedroom and was shocked to find her with her knees on the floor and arms on the bed. She looked up at me with confusion as if she wanted to say, "Help! I don't know what happened, and I don't know what to do."

It was a gut punch, a new glimpse inside the helplessness of her world, a measure of vulnerability I didn't know before that moment but was facing squarely, and I could do nothing but acknowledge it. Just as I found a little peace after processing another loss of Carol's personality, memories, habits, and capabilities, a new loss appeared. It was a double whammy; I acknowledged a new piece of Carol was lost while being harshly reminded that more would follow until no pieces remained. I was reminded of Sisyphus of Greek mythology, condemned by Zeus to roll a massive boulder up a hill only for it to roll back down as he neared the top. He was fated to repeat this action for all eternity. My penchant for drama notwithstanding, there were times when watching my wife suffer with FTD was a raw burden that was maddening and seemed unending. I knew this was fodder for meditation. My life was rolling a boulder up a mountain, watching it roll down, and then doing it again. It was okay.

I helped Carol back into bed, and Tina came into the room to start her day. I returned to my office, still feeling the ache of the incident, sat behind my desk, and began meditating on my thoughts and emotions, incorporating The Six Realities.

When practicing meditation, I must be willing to be with whatever comes up: conceit, avarice, desire, agony, anxiety, fear, happiness, or joy. Being with these emotions, witnessing them, makes me aware of my attachments, and going over them repeatedly eventually begins to dissolve them. It helps me become nonattached and loving. This is transforming my core, and in turn, my anxieties continue to diminish.

In my relationship with Carol, meditation was clarifying how much she needed me and depended on me for her quality of life. It was cultivating our intimacy, and I wanted to provide for her as best as possible. The more I experienced joy, the more I saw it spreading into my relationships with others. It was not that my life was transformed, but it was transforming, I didn't know if it would ever be completely transformed.

I was not trying to reach perfection, because what life was for me each day was perfection, and I worked on what was given to me. I was a work in progress that would never be complete. There was no end point, but practicing meditation with the daily challenges and crises I faced were opening my life. An internal shift was happening, and I developed confidence in my ability to cope with life's tragedies.

Anthony P. Mauro Sr.

The City Kids

When I was growing up in Monmouth Beach, during the summer, several families from Jersey City rented the large Victorian homes that lined the beaches, seeking respite from the city's heat, traffic, noise, and congestion. They were big families with lots of kids who we affectionately called "city kids."

I was always excited when they arrived, because I usually had a crush on one of them. The object of my crush might change from year to year or even from day to day, but there was always one I couldn't wait to see walking around town. I had butterflies in my stomach and felt jolts of electricity when seeing my crush du jour. I was too shy to let my feelings be known at that point in life, but it didn't diminish the power of my emotions and may have even played upon them.

When the city kids arrived in late May, I understood that their time in town was limited. In three months, the girl I liked would be gone, and I'd have to wait nine months for her return. Instead of dreading the briefness of her stay and crossing off each passing day on the calendar, I was focused on enjoying her for as long as she was in town. I didn't know about meditation at the time, and I was consumed by awkwardness and self-doubt, but I was able to enjoy something even though I knew it would go away—the transient "city girl." This same awareness grows with practicing meditation.

Seeing Carol hanging from our bed was painful, but meditation helped me see that future moments were not guaranteed for anyone, that FTD was a part of our life, and that I had to enjoy our time together. Like the city girl, the summer would end. Life is impermanent.

UTIs

A few weeks after Carol fell out of bed, I went into our bedroom to wake her up. She opened her eyes and looked at me, but she was subdued, as she usually smiled or giggled when she saw me. I greeted her with my usual question, "How did you sleep last night?" and she responded, "I slept good!" with a rising pitch on the word "good."

I had difficulty getting her out of bed. She wasn't moving her legs, she wouldn't sit upright, and she wasn't clapping, which was the sign I relied on to know she was alert and happy. That day, she looked as if she was in a state between sleeping and waking—a dazed, bewildered, hypnotic condition, unresponsive to my presence. I asked her to swing her legs over the side of the bed and took her hands to help her sit upright. She looked at me with a blank stare.

I looked down and noticed that her hands were shaking. When she was finally sitting upright, she wasn't clapping. She just sat, looking bewildered. I asked if anything was bothering her, but there was no response. I helped her to her feet, but she wobbled and dropped back onto the bed. I asked again if she felt okay, and she said yes, but yes and no answers were standard for her and weren't proven to be reliable. I waited a few moments and encouraged her to get up again. I held her as she made her way to the bathroom, but her walk was unsteady.

I was beginning to worry. Thoughts flooded my mind: *What will I do if she becomes paralyzed? How will I care for her? What if she can't descend the flight of stairs? Is she entering a new phase of decline? What should I expect in the future?* With each round of rumination, my fear mounted. By that time, I was instinctively practicing meditation, witnessing each thought as it occurred as well as the emotions and body sensations that stirred.

I took Carol to her local doctor, but she had no answer. I then contacted Dr. Devi and mentioned that Carol's urine had a powerful odor that was different than usual. A lab test for a urinary tract infection (UTI) was prescribed. It took two days to get the urine sample, as Carol was incontinent and couldn't urinate on demand. The test was positive for a UTI.

I was happy that Dr. Devi was willing to help, although treating a UTI was not the responsibility of a neurologist. She prescribed antibiotic medicine and told me I must keep Carol hydrated. Carol was back to feeling herself in a few days.

This wasn't Carol's first UTI, but it was the first that presented such pronounced symptoms: confusion, a change in her behavior, and withdrawal. Since she couldn't communicate how she felt, it was a guessing game to uncover.

After the last UTI, Carol's gynecologist had told me that she would no longer test her, and I needed to take Carol to a urologist in the future for infections. It was difficult for me to get the urine samples, and I needed to have a specimen cup handy at the right place and right time.

Doctor and lab visits were problematic for Carol, and taking her to an additional doctor would only make life more uncomfortable for her. UTIs are prevalent with people who have FTD. Carol had shown that she couldn't communicate when she wasn't feeling well.

Managing doctors and their ignorance of Carol's condition or resistance to dealing with it became problematic. I wasn't sure how I was going to handle it. I began to investigate alternative ways to provide comfortable care for Carol by doctors knowledgeable about her condition, ideally a place where I could get most primary care services.

Something Smells Fishy

I had just returned from an errand and put my keys on the kitchen counter. I was happy to see that Tina's sister, Mari, was visiting. She was a pleasant woman who spoke English well, so it was easier for me to strike up a conversation with her (Tina's English was broken). The two of them talked so much in Georgian that I had to stand ready to find a way to butt in.

I said something, and when I paused, Tina filled in the conversational gap by politely criticizing me for not cleaning the counter thoroughly. I was proud of my attempt at wiping kitchen counter debris, since I knew that my every move in the home was inspected and a mental note taken, but apparently the salmon I had for dinner the night before had left a foul bouquet that lingered on the counter. Not that I could detect such a remnant, but I was told there was a stench, period! Not wanting to miss an opportunity, Tina pointed out that there was also evidence of the stink on the sponge I had used.

I didn't feel the need to defend myself, partly because my nose was sensitive enough to pick up anything uninviting and partly because it was my kitchen. I responded with a polite smile and moved on to say hello to Carol, who was sitting a few feet away. I guess my gracious grin was a matter of interpretation, because the next comment I heard was about how I hadn't cleaned the dishes properly before I put them in the dishwasher.

At that point, my grin wasn't as gracious and couldn't be mistaken for anything otherwise, but I was practicing meditation as the drama unfolded, which was probably why I didn't send Tina packing for her homeland.

Lights Out

On another occasion, a light bulb burned out in a chandelier over the kitchen table. It was a five-bulb chandelier, so four bulbs were working and providing light. I didn't give any urgency to replacing the bulb and hadn't realized that my lack of urgency didn't meet Tina's expectations. She admonished me. From that moment on, I was on DEFCON 1 alert for light bulb readiness, or at least I gave that impression.

It was obvious that Tina and I bickered, but practicing meditation helped me see that it was healthy. We were individuals from diverse cultures, traditions, and upbringings, and I was thirty years older. It was like an arranged marriage of two people thrown together who knew nothing about each other. Put in this context, the bickering was normal. We had diverse ways of doing things from cleaning house and doing chores to our general ways of life. One minute we were arguing, but in another, we were finding a way to laugh. I think this helped to create a bond. It provided a way to navigate the relationship and settle bigger disputes, at least for me. In some way, I appreciated that Tina didn't feel as if she was a servant in our home. Importantly, she put Carol first, catered to her needs, and quietly dealt with the frustrations of caring for a person with FTD. She always did things that were over and above the job description.

One day she took on the herculean task of cleaning out Carol's closet and reorganizing it. To give an idea of how enthusiastically she approached the project, I spent more on wooden, white-painted replacement clothes hangers than I did on groceries each week. It was Tina's way of showing that Carol deserved the best quality. The hangers I used were white too, but they were made of plastic and cost less than a burger and fries.

Making House Calls

It was a warm Saturday morning in May, and I slowly opened my eyes to sunlight in the bedroom—a rare occurrence, since I always rose before the sun got around to doing the same. The window in our bedroom was open because of the warm weather that lingered from the day before. I felt that this day would be the same. As I broke through the fog of sleep, I found myself staring at the ceiling, enjoying the indulgence of sleeping late and the snugness of being in bed.

I was listening to the cooing of a mourning dove. When I was young, the same sound would wake me, like a gracious alarm clock, to warm summer days and the excitement of being on a three-month break from school. Some people say it is a low, sorrowful sound that signifies melancholy, but to this day I take comfort in it as if it's a spiritual message to find inner peace and love, a catalyst to begin a healing process, or a gentle reminder to find harmony in my life.

The experience inspired a moment of clarity. As I reminisced about waking to the sound of a mourning dove as a boy, my thoughts jumped to being sick one summer day and how the doctor made a house call to see me. Back then it was the norm, but I hadn't heard of such a practice for sixty years. I thought that medical house calls would be ideal for Carol's situation: no waiting rooms and no need to disrupt her routine. It would be a personalized experience for her condition and symptoms while in the setting of her home.

I threw back the covers and started to research. As I looked through a medical directory, I saw doctors who specialized in geriatric medicine, which helped me focus on that area. After a little more research, I found a local primary care practice that made old-fashioned house calls specifically for older adults and homebound patients. Its staff included physicians, physician assistants, and nurse practitioners, all with experience in adult and geriatric care. This approach would allow Carol to stay at home and improve her quality of life. I hired the service.

By this time, I had been meditating for one and a half years and saw that progress happened in phases. I'd go through one phase and find myself at another level of awareness about myself and life. The fact was that I was presented with small annoyances practically every day: pettiness, jealousy, betrayal, disappointment, deadline stresses, and dealing with people who were angry, unjust, or unfair. Meditation gave me a way to adapt to the tensions, but it kept me in a phase of progress or level of awareness for months.

The biggest advance in my awareness was when a crisis or trauma arose and I had to practice meditation about the swirling thoughts, intense fear, and anxiety. These usually involved Carol and a significant progression of the FTD.

I experienced the biggest eternal shifts when meditating on the hardest circumstances life presented. As a result, my awareness of reality expanded. I could hold more of life, and my life was opening.

I began to understand that given my advanced age, I faced the increased likelihood of accidents, illnesses, and traumatic events. This awareness caused thoughts, feelings, and changes that I used for practicing meditation.

I noticed that a period of progress was followed by a regression or setback caused by major stressors. One such moment was on its way.

Never, Never on a Sunday

It was 5:00 a.m. on a June morning. I was sleeping in bed next to Carol. My alarm wasn't set because it was Sunday, but a loud, terrifying, indescribable noise jolted me awake. I shot upright, still dopey, my eyes darting left and right, trying to find the source of a racket so close I sensed it could reach out and touch me.

I turned to Carol and saw from the outline of the bedcovers draping her body that her arms and legs were stiff. I jumped from bed and rushed to her side. Her head was shaking, her eyelids locked open, pupils dilated, and skin pale. Her blank stare conveyed that she was unaware of my presence. She was making guttural noises and gasping for air. It seemed like she was struggling with every ounce of effort to fill her lungs. I tried to open her mouth to see if there was an obstruction, but her jaws were clenched and unyielding.

In a panic, I told her she would be all right and I loved her, not knowing if these were the last words she would hear.

Her phone was on her nightstand next to me, so I picked it up to call 911, but the app was frozen and didn't respond. I dropped the phone, jumped to my side of the bed, grabbed my iPhone, and stabbed at the numbers 911. As the phone rang, I told her again that I loved her.

It took ten minutes for the EMTs to arrive, and by that time, Carol was becoming responsive. Her lip was cut and bleeding but not so much that it needed special attention. Not knowing what had happened and the possibility it had been a stroke, I told the ambulance driver to ignore two nearby hospitals and take us to a Level II trauma center twenty minutes away, known for treating stroke and heart failure.

As we rode to the hospital, I looked at Carol on the stretcher. She was quiet but didn't appear to be in any pain. Her skin color had returned to normal, the EMT attending her said her vital signs were okay, and she was resting. It was the first moment I had to collect my thoughts.

I realized it was a Sunday morning and remembered from working in the healthcare industry decades earlier that the quality of hospital care was typically lower on weekends.

After meeting with a hospital executive I knew well, I had asked the off-topic question about the noticeable difference in the level of care on weekends. He said that staff coverage tended to be lighter, and the professionals working typically had less seniority and experience. He also said that delays in treatments were caused because diagnostic services weren't open, physicians arrived later in the day, and they waited until the next morning to check on the results of tests they had ordered. As a result, the pace of medical care on weekends slowed from a run to a walk, and many stable patients were kept in emergency room beds.

We arrived at the hospital at 5:45 a.m., and Carol was admitted. She was given a bed in the emergency room and remained there until nearly 10:00 p.m. She was in good spirits during those sixteen hours and was kept comfortable, but it took hours for a doctor to examine her. I gave a nurse a list of her medications, dosages, and the times she took them.

Carol was finally assigned and moved to a room at 10:00 p.m. I got a comfortable chair and asked a nurse for a blanket since I would be staying with Carol. That I was staying overnight surprised the staff, and because Carol had a female roommate, I was told that a male sleeping in the same room was not allowed, so they moved us to a private room. It was nice of them to be accommodating, and there was a couch for me to sleep on, so I was especially grateful.

The staff may have wondered why I stayed with Carol 24-7, but from my perspective, it couldn't have been more obvious. Carol could not articulate when something was bothering her or she felt sick. Given my experience, I usually understood the cues from her that others might overlook and could relay them to the staff.

Nurses approached me on more than one occasion to go over the list of Carol's medicines, and they got them wrong on two separate occasions. If I hadn't been present, Carol would not have been able to correct them. I was concerned that Carol's restless behavior, clapping, tapping, impulsiveness, and need to walk around would be problematic in a hospital setting. I knew the way they would manage these was sedation. Dr. Devi had told me early on in Carol's diagnosis that sedation could have a negative impact on FTD patients, possibly accelerating brain degeneration, and I was going to make sure that sedation for managing her fidgety behavior wasn't an option. This was the main reason for staying with her, and there were times doctors and nurses relied on me for advice and information that Carol could not provide herself.

I had yet to receive any information regarding the cause of Carol's condition, so an MRI was ordered to help with a diagnosis. At 1:00 a.m., they rolled her bed to the room for the MRI, and I remained in the waiting area. I agreed to the MRI, but the test relied on Carol being completely still for twenty minutes to ensure accuracy. Since she couldn't understand this requirement to keep motionless, I felt it was in her best interest to be mildly sedated. The decision was really made by itself; the doctors needed a precise image.

Carol slept most of the following day. She was in such a stupor from the sedative that the staff had difficulty waking her to be fed and to check on her progress. At one point, a doctor came to exam Carol but couldn't wake her. Confused, the doctor turned to me with a look that sought the answer. This was not Carol's normal condition. I had no answer other than it being the effect of the sedative. I walked over to her bed, and Carol awakened, perhaps because she recognized my voice.

A CT scan for imaging the brain and an EEG to measure electrical activity were also ordered, tests that didn't require Carol to be sedated. Inconceivably, I didn't have the test results until the fourth day of our stay but should have had them within twenty-four hours according to one of the nurses caring for Carol. The diagnosis was that Carol had suffered a seizure, but there was no explanation as to what caused it or whether it was related to FTD. I had never seen a seizure before, but it left an indelible impression. A nurse gave me instructions for overseeing Carol should it recur, and she was discharged.

As I drove home, I cynically reminded myself never to get seriously injured or sick on a weekend, but I was happy that Carol was sitting next to me, unscarred by the event. I was also thinking about how hard it was to watch her suffer, so much so that I'd rather switch places with her. I think it would be easier for me. Caring for someone who is helpless is an enormous responsibility, and it is exhausting. This wasn't the first time I found myself asking profoundly painful questions like why Carol had FTD and not me. Why could I enjoy life and she couldn't? What else could I do when I knew I couldn't do anything to change things? Why did I feel I was never doing enough?

Over the years, I had a sense of indignation about this situation. I complained to myself that it wasn't fair and Carol didn't deserve such treatment. I deliberated on the fact that an injustice has befallen her. It was hard to watch this injustice play out, and it caused my heart to ache. It was a constant reminder of the fragility of life.

There Are No Kids Like Grandkids

Carol and I celebrated July Fourth with Anthony Jr., Tori, and our two grandchildren. Charli was seven months old, and AJ was one month old. A year and a half earlier, Carol was playfully harassing Tori to give her a grandchild, and Tori politely responded that she had no intention of having children and her decision was unchangeable. Even ironclad decisions are casualties of impermanence, and six months after saying this, she announced that she was pregnant.

In the time before this festive family gathering, Carol lost a level of understanding what a grandchild meant to her. The special bond she envisioned having with grandchildren gave way to the progress of FTD, and she was mildly indifferent to their presence. Although she still had a wonderfully happy demeanor, she responded less to the emotional expressions of her children, her grandchildren, and me. She wasn't cold but distant, less socially engaged, and the warmth of her personality was fading as was her empathy. She was becoming quieter and more withdrawn.

Even before our kids were married, Carol had talked about how much she looked forward to having grandchildren. She wanted to experience the special bond, love, and joy that would come with watching them explore the world around them, listening to their little voices babble, playing with them, holding them, and savoring their hugs and kisses. She wanted to build her relationship with them without being the rule enforcer she had been with her own kids. She wanted the sweet revisiting of a time when her children were small and bloomed into caring adults and great parents. She wanted to be able to step in and assist, to be counted on for love and experience, to buy them toys, and to pick out clothes.

Though it seemed that her ability to enjoy her grandkids was waning, I placed Charli in Carol's arms as she sat on the couch. She didn't say anything, didn't try to hug her, didn't seem to have a rush of thoughts, feelings, or gratitude, but she did look at the baby, then at me, and smile. This smile was enough for me to see that on some level she was touched by the moment, and for that I was grateful.

Ritualistic behaviors were becoming more pronounced. Carol became restless and went through fixed routes in our home. She'd be watching TV and suddenly walk to a window, peer out, start clapping, then move to our kitchen table and tap on the top rail of a chair, move on to another chair, and do the same. She repeated this compulsion so often that the stain on the chairs was stripped and the wood exposed.

Sometimes she walked out on our back deck and went to a corner to pause, look at the back yard, erupt into a burst of happy claps, and return inside. Other times, she grabbed her purse and walked to the back door as if she was headed out to be with a friend or to go shopping. I had special locks installed so she couldn't open doors and go outside on her own and door alarms and cameras installed so I could monitor her movements.

The clapping, tapping on the kitchen chairs and on her iPhone, and rubbing her hands together were habitual, but they were done with enthusiasm, a broad smile, and a glint in her eye that made each episode an endearing performance.

Although I knew FTD was progressive, the changes were always hard to watch. The disease was slow and steady, ample evidence that FTD would eventually win the race. It was just a matter of time. FTD was the fabled slow-moving tortoise in the race with the hare.

Practicing meditation was also like being a slow-moving tortoise. I fumbled my way through trying to make a connection with something that could be unclear but I sensed existed. The commitment to practicing meditation in everything I did all day with every frustration, jealousy, resentment, inconvenience, and fear that arose provided the fragments that went into creating the larger connection to freedom, joy, wisdom, understanding, compassion, and fun.

Cleaning House

Over the years, practice causes the faint effacement of unreality and ignorance, and in turn, reality is gradually revealed. I am beginning to flow with life. It is not that things are added to my life that bring about a sense of freedom but instead the absence of things.

It's as if my ego or lesser self is a house, and I compulsively hoard thoughts and emotions. I am resistant to discarding the heaps of belongings. In this case, my "belongings" are not old newspapers, junk, unopened mail, garbage, and things that will never be used again but my attachments, desire, anger, sorrow, revenge, and pain. These things have no value but are the emotional clutter to which I attach myself, and they fill up the living space of my house.

Anthony P. Mauro Sr.

Practicing meditation is the bit-by-bit removal of these attachments. Some items are tiny and more easily thrown away, but others are so big and bulky that they need a lot of time to break down and carry away. To remove most of the clutter might take years, and it will take effort and commitment. At first, it doesn't seem as if progress is being made, but over time, I'm able to step back and see a bit of space that couldn't be seen before. This space expands over the years.

I don't work on discarding my house for a new one. I *am* my house, and removing clutter allows me the freedom to move about it. I am free to be myself. Disorder becomes order. The clutter that makes a maze of my life begins to clear, and I start to flow along with life. Carol still has FTD, but a transformation is occurring. I am more open to the situation, learning from it, and handling it better.

A Brief Mental Health Crisis

In July, a mental health crisis happened like the one I had when I was twenty-five. It drove home the point that practicing meditation had no end game.

It had been four years since Carol's diagnosis. During this time, I cared for her every day, maintained our home, fed us three meals a day, managed my business, shopped for groceries, coordinated her medical needs, took her on doctor appointments, helped our kids cope with their mom's FTD, and handled the little demands that made up our lives together.

I have been fortunate most of my life in that I rarely have trouble sleeping at night. I usually hit the pillow and am out until jolted awake by the rudeness of my alarm clock. I had no reason to believe this night would be any different until it was.

It was 1:00 a.m., and I snapped out of sleep. My breathing was shallow, and I felt like I was being suffocated. I was stunned and confused. I got out of bed, and my legs were weak. I felt faint and for a moment thought I would drop to the floor. I was sweating, the type of sweat that is created by a fight-or-flight scenario. I felt as if I was trying to survive a nerve-wracking drama but had no idea what the drama was.

It took a bit before I came to my senses and realized it was a panic attack. I relied on the calming method I used for managing them, and it eventually subsided. I returned to bed and meditated on my thoughts and the residue of intense fear, but the fear was so overwhelming that it was difficult to stay with it for long. I eventually was able to go back to sleep, but it was a light, restless sleep.

I woke up worried about whether depression, agoraphobia, and panic attacks would recur, because I wasn't sure how I'd take care of Carol. I had Tina to help, but it still was a major concern that added stress to my situation. I could only imagine that it was a culmination of stressors and perhaps had a biological/chemical cause. As I started the day, I had difficulty concentrating on work and coping with my responsibilities. I wasn't functioning effectively, had to force myself to eat, and felt overwhelmed and irritable. My mind and body were craving rest. This was a shock, because meditation had made such a positive difference in lowering my anxiety.

After a few days, I was able to compose myself and meditated on my thoughts and emotions. I had plenty to witness and experience, as life played the role of teacher and was confronting me with what I needed to confront. I'd had a mental health crisis before, but now I was okay living with it and wasn't trying to hide or suppress it. I understood myself and saw the nature of my reaction to what was happening to me. I recognized there was nothing from the outside assaulting me, only my thoughts, attachments, and wants.

After two weeks of practicing with intense anxiety, I began to feel better, and after a few more weeks, I returned to a place of freedom and calm. I remembered that the first time I had a similar crisis, it took me nearly three years to recuperate, so this was a dramatic difference in time and quality. The difficulties I encountered *were* life.

Practice is witnessing the way I do things, how I operate in my life, how I do my job, how I relate to my kids, how I am with my friends or strangers, how I respond to someone being disrespectful, and what I think and feel when in the company of someone I don't like. I don't have to stop whatever I'm doing, but witnessing and acknowledging my thoughts, emotions, and body sensations makes them less shadowy, and I become less engaged with them.

One Man's Blanket Is Another Man's iPhone

It was a sweltering August day, the kind that made your clothes soggy even when sitting motionless in the shade. There were no clouds, so as the sun reached brilliance by midday, it caused roads to shimmer and warp. I saw an unfortunate dog in a neighbor's yard trotting toward shelter with its tongue hanging and flopping, synchronized with the bounce in its stride.

It was the kind of day where local news stations did stories about people frying eggs on sidewalks and "man on the street" interviews with cameras focused on flushed faces, ridiculous questions, and obvious answers about how it felt to be a hot mess.

Fortunately, when we bought our home, it came with an old pool. I had some work done to it so that it was usable, and for many years, Carol enjoyed lazily floating on an inflatable pool mat, the kind she could lounge on. The blue shapes on the pool siding and floor made the crystal-clear water appear as blue as the sky. It was soothing for the eyes and had a refreshing effect on the mind and body. Our kids used to dive and splash with eyes closed and hearts open into the water. Carol's preference was to maintain a sense of dignity and use the stairs to lower herself into the water.

It was difficult for Carol to get on the floating pool mat by herself, but she still wanted to enjoy the pool. I helped her get in by positioning the mat at the top step, and she let the circulating water take her where it willed. This was in stark contrast to a year earlier when she was able to get herself on and off the mat. Now, she looked uneasy, like she didn't want to move a muscle, but when I asked if she wanted to stay in the pool, she said yes. I remained in the pool with her the entire time.

Eventually I saw that Carol was looking uncomfortable on the pool mat, so I took her over to the steps and helped her off. I helped her down the steps so that she could cool off in the waist-high water, and after a few minutes, I took her inside to change out of her bathing suit into dry clothes.

When I was helping to get her ready for bed, I realized that she had forgotten her iPhone outside. It was the first day she forgot her phone and would be the last day she remembered to have it with her. I made sure she had it when we left the house and always made sure she had it next to her while watching TV or when we went on walks. She enjoyed holding her phone, though I had to operate the apps for her.

Any exuberance she felt, which often came in impulsive bursts, was demonstrated by her happily tapping the face of the phone, so I knew that in some way it had importance to her. She carried her iPhone wherever she went. I didn't know if it was a link to the expansive world she once knew, a thing that provided comfort and security, or an item that made her feel a sense of control or gave it some type of meaning. The iPhone seemed like Carol's version of the blanket Linus Van Pelt of the *Peanuts* comic strip carried. As life changed, the blanket, or iPhone in this case, provided reassurance.

At this point in the progression of the FTD, monosyllabic answers of yes or no were predominantly Carol's spoken form of communication. If I gave her a choice between one thing or another, she almost always repeated the last option. It was increasingly difficult to know what she wanted, how she wanted it, or even if she wanted it. Most of the time she went along with whatever decision was made, but I still wanted her to have a sense of control over her life, even if it mattered only to me.

Coffee and Cigarettes

November is a time I finish any plans or projects that I have for the year, and this year was no different. It's also officially Banana Pudding Lovers Month, though I'm certainly no fan of the concoction. Today it seems that even the most ordinary thing has its own official day.

My immediate assignment was to welcome a replacement for Tina. She had to return to her native country and would be gone at least a year. Fortunately, before leaving, she set me up with Nina, who committed to working six months with Carol before returning to Georgia.

The women from Georgia seem to have a blend of Balkan and Slavic features. It is a unique look, but describing it beyond what I have escapes my vocabulary. They guard their modesty and, as far as I could tell, mostly belong to the Orthodox Church of Georgia, which had a traditional approach to religion. The one thing I noticed was that they could exist solely on coffee and cigarettes.

They also seem to take pride in their hair, perhaps a sign of their femininity in their native land. They diligently care for it, and I never met one whose hair was not long and lush. Most seem talkative. Nina didn't speak much English, but I would overhear her chatting in her native tongue on the phone a lot during her off hours.

Having an outsider live in my home was now a normal part of life. The women weren't at all intrusive. They would take care of Carol and, at day's end, retreat to their room. I hardly heard from them until it was time to start the next day or when they went outside for a smoke. I surprised myself in that I was able to adapt to strangers living in my home, but these strangers became like family. I cared about their lives and the lives of their families.

All the caregivers who worked with Carol went beyond the job description. They treated her as if she was part of their own family. I didn't know if it was out of a sense of fairness, their religious belief, or a desire for a "just world." They asked me why such a happy, loving, caring woman like Carol was chosen to suffer with FTD—a thought I had meditated on for some time.

Where Do We Get the Energy to Do It?

I think back to looking out the window of the train, taking Carol to New York City to see Dr. Devi, and the hidden world of an interdependent ecosystem: food chains, a food web, plants, and wildlife.

I was looking at a system that transfers life-sustaining energy from living things to living things through predator-and-prey relationships. These relationships range from the microbial food web that is a main driver of the biogeochemical cycles to mammals such as coyotes that prey on rabbits, mice, and other small animals. Prey die, and the energy contained in the carcass is transferred to the predator that feeds on it so that it may use the energy to live. As predator and prey go about their business, they participate in what appears to be a consciously designed and orchestrated ecosystem that uses the energy of living things to provide an interdependent, balanced, healthy environment. Consciousness is a force in these living things. It is a changing field of energy.

I am an ever-changing, impermanent energy field too. Is my energy more important than another creature's energy? I may think so, but I'm not sure that other creatures or people would agree. I'm also sure it makes little difference to life. I am just atoms in a cog that composes life's wheel, and like all other living things that have occupied earth, I will die. I suffer when thinking I am more important than other living things, because it blinds me to the inevitable.

When I founded a conservation organization with the mission of educating state legislators about the sustainable use of natural resources, one area I discussed was the importance of forest regeneration. This is the process by which tree seedlings become established after forests have died from fire, insects, disease, or being felled by winds. The destruction of the forests is needed to regenerate ecosystems that support all sorts of life.

Explaining how parts of a forest must be destroyed by nature in order for it to sustain itself and thrive defies our eyes. It is a paradox. It takes death to sustain life, but change like this is not what we want. We want to keep things as we see them, as we want them to be. Our ignorance of life has us resisting the changes that life presents us. We resist impermanence and attach ourselves to the things we want in life even though life behaves otherwise. As a result, we create anxiety, worry, depression, and other unhealthy conditions. Attachment is refusing to see the truth.

Life seems harsh, but there is intelligence in its survival design, and this intelligence is hard to see up close. We must take a step back so that the grand design comes into view. It's like practicing meditation. We "step back" when witnessing and acknowledging our thoughts, emotions, and body sensations. It provides the bigger picture of ourselves, and a bigger picture of life and our place in it comes into view.

When it comes to Carol, as seductive as it is to carry around my unrealized dreams and feel my anger while raising my clenched fist and accusing the heavens of unfairness, the truth is that these feelings are poisonous to me and do not change reality. There is only Carol's condition and no denying that we are all going to die.

Just Think About It

Something spiritual is happening as I witness my mind and body, but I've asked myself, *Who is the "I" doing the witnessing?* Is it a higher consciousness working in and through me? Is it the greater self? Is consciousness energy? Is it the dimension that makes everything functional in our world and that created existence, an existence capable of instinct and consciousness in living things?

Instinct is a natural, inherent impulse or behavior, while consciousness is the state of being conscious or aware. People say that a dog has instinct and not consciousness, but is it consciousness that allows a dog to understand the difference between being tripped over or purposely kicked? I think so.

Is it the force or energy of consciousness within the environment that makes the food web functional? It seems to me that the "witness" in us that observes thoughts, emotions, and body sensations is the consciousness that flows through all living things. The degree to which each creature can access this force or consciousness may vary, humans having it to the greatest extent.

Once I understood the universal aspect of consciousness, I began to see that my suffering was inherently the same as the suffering of other people and all living things. As my life began to open through meditation, it also opened to an awareness to all life.

In this sense, I am not independent from the homeless, poor, wealthy, ill, egotistical, shy, kings, queens, trees, or any creature. I rely on living things for food (plants and animals) and use their energy so that I may survive. We are all participants in life. With this understanding comes wisdom and compassion, which is shared with all people and things. Because of the awareness, we are connected.

Growth from practicing meditation means starving anxiety. No nourishment goes to the dysfunctional mental programs I created as a child to protect me from pain, suffering, fear, and the need for approval and love.

A Turkey and Password

It was the fourth Thursday in November, a day that Americans tolerate traffic jams, survive flight delays, eat themselves into a coma, and put up with other stresses to spend time with family and friends. It was a day that lifted spirits in our household, and Carol being in the kitchen always made it extra special. Thanksgiving was a day of abundant appetizers, a salad, homemade stuffing, a turkey entrée, side dishes, desserts, and drinks.

Last year, Anthony Jr., Gina, Tori, and Andrew brought all the ingredients to our home and prepared the meal for the first time. They wanted to honor and give back what Carol had given them. An atmosphere of excitement and a "we can do this" attitude electrified the celebration. They wanted to recreate the feast their mother had provided for many years, and they did so exceptionally.

The house was filled with mouthwatering aromas, fun conversation, open photo albums and recollecting memories, platters of food, a bustling atmosphere, and a pinch of stress added by those wanting to ensure a perfect meal. The whole family was gathered comfortably near, though at times, the chefs in the kitchen complained that I was too comfortably near. A patchwork of personalities made up the family: the adventurous, the active, the assertive, the anxious, and the affable.

The joyous amalgamation of sights, sounds, and scents created a warm atmosphere, enhanced by the roaring fire in the family room. Once the assortment of recipes disappeared from our plates, we dug into the best homemade cookies and pies ever baked. Every Thanksgiving, I promised myself not to eat too much, a resolution I never lived up to. By day's end, I wanted to roll into bed and sleep away the food in my distended stomach.

This year, I had the food catered so that we could get the most out of enjoying each other's company. The pace of things in our home without meal preparation was also less hectic and, I felt, less of a distraction to Carol.

When you peel away the trimmings of Thanksgiving, it is the people who join you that matter.

Carol was sitting on the couch, watching TV. I noticed she had left her iPhone on the kitchen table, so I walked over to give it to her. She usually entered her password and began fumbling with the apps that appeared. It was still an everyday experience for her to accidentally delete the few apps she liked using, and I would reload them for her. On this day, she forgot the password to the phone, which might be a slip of the mind for any of us, but her password was her birthdate. She couldn't sign in without help from that point forward.

This was one of the developments that hit me hard, even harder than when she no longer remembered to keep a watchful eye on her handbag. This was more fodder for meditation.

Good Things Can Come from Not So Good Things

At this time, Nina came to me and said her mother, who lived in Georgia, needed to have heart surgery. She would leave in a matter of days to care for her and didn't know of a replacement, so I scrambled to find a new caregiver.

I used an internet site for caregivers who represented themselves without an agent. There were pros and cons to using an agency to hire caregivers just as there were to doing it personally. The pros were having more control in choosing who would live with us, the freedom to assign tasks and duties, and not having to pay a fee to an agent or go through them with every requirement and issue. The cons were that I had to do the interviews myself, check the candidate's background, and determine whether the person had the right skill set for Carol. If the person quit, I had to go through the process all over again.

Interestingly, the person I hired became ill before she started but recommended an associate of hers, Lika. Sometimes life has a way of turning a setback into success, and this was one of those cases.

Lika had many cultural characteristics of Georgian women, but her personality and qualities were exceptional in caring for Carol and being a part of our family. After living with us for one month, it was evident that Lika was considerate, empathetic, respectful, and polite. In short, she loved Carol. We talked about numerous subjects, she could see the world beyond herself, and she derived joy and satisfaction from caring for Carol. She had Carol's best interests at heart. She knew what others were feeling and responded accordingly, had a sense of humor, and was well educated.

A Time for Goodbye

I received a phone call from Carol's sister, Lynn, with the news that their mother, Marion, had passed. She was in her mid-nineties and in assisted living due to Alzheimer's disease.

FTD and Alzheimer's are different. Dr. Devi said the people who show signs of Alzheimer's tend to be those older than sixty-five, and the risk increases with age. FTD, on the other hand, usually starts between the ages of forty-five and sixty-four. There are differences in the affected cognitive functions, personality changes, location of brain lesions, and symptoms. Regarding Alzheimer's disease, the first symptoms are memory problems and disorientation. With FTD, the first symptoms are personality changes and disinhibition.

I didn't think the news of her mother's passing would have much of a visible impact on Carol. A few weeks earlier, I had told her that her mother wasn't doing well, and she had no reaction. Grief is natural and normal following the loss of a loved one, but FTD and other forms of dementia complicate this process. I imagined trivial lies had their place in simplifying life and calming anxious or agitated loved ones, but this matter didn't involve a little white lie.

Carol hadn't spoken to her mother in several years. Given this history, I broke the news to her the morning her mom died, and as expected, her reaction was an impulsive giggle. She laughed at many things that people might find inappropriate, and though this might be troubling to some, I took comfort in the fact that she was happy and didn't seem to experience the pain of losing her mother.

Carol didn't have a reaction during the funeral service. She spent the time doing the trivial things she did each day: clapping, tapping, counting her steps, giggling, and whatever else occurred in her beautiful mind that wasn't knowable to the rest of us.

When it came time to lay a flower on her mother's casket, a symbol of love and affection, Carol did so without saying a word or changing her expression. We were the last of the family members to enact this tradition, and we then joined the rest of the family a few feet away. As we turned to leave, I had Carol's arm in mine, and I felt her tugging in the opposite direction. She started to walk back to the casket, and I went along with her. She stood and paused for a moment but said nothing. No facial expressions betrayed what she might have been thinking. After a few moments, she turned, and I led her back to her family.

THE YEAR 2023

Make Her Happy

I don't know the psychology behind a man wanting to make a woman laugh, but I know it's important to me, and I take pleasure in seeing Carol laugh so hard that her body shakes. I think anyone can make us cry, but it takes someone special to make us laugh. Laughter creates a bond, a sense of togetherness. In some small way, it also keeps our relationships fresh and breaks up boredom. Carol's laugh is contagious for me.

Every night I take her for a ride and do antics to get her to smile. I can't use my cleverness to make her smile anymore, so I rely on silly sounds or invented words to get a reaction. I must work hard and be persistent before my humor registers in her eyes and she relents with a giggle. Not too long ago after a witticism, she'd say, "You're funny, you're funny." I haven't heard the phrase recently. I imagine it's due to the FTD degeneration, like so many of her wonderful traits that have disappeared.

Our nightly walks and Jeep rides usually last forty-five minutes, and we travel the same route. There is one place along our ride where she turns to me and says, "You're a good driver." She declares it at the exact same spot at a turn in the road. One night, she didn't say it, and I never heard it again.

To remember the specialness of the spot, when we approach it, I say, "Who is the best passenger in the world?" She responds gleefully, "Me." It is a cute response, especially because she was so modest before the FTD diagnosis that she would never make such a shameless proclamation. I was so happy with the self-confidence in her answer that I concocted a few more questions for her to answer to make her feel good about herself.

Though Lika gets her ready for bed, I always tuck Carol under the covers. As her head rests on the pillow, I kneel next to her, and we look eye to eye. I ask her the same four questions.

"Who's the best woman in the world?" She replies with delight, "Me!"

"Who's the best mother in the world?" Again, with spirit, "Me!"

"Who's the best wife in the world?" She says, "Me!"

I repeat what I asked during our Jeep ride: "Who's the best passenger in the world?" Without any loss in enthusiasm, she states, "Me!"

It makes me happy to know that she feels good about herself.

I open Find My on her iPhone so she can see the whereabouts of our children. She reads out their locations which, at the hour she goes to bed, are the towns where they live. I ask her, "Is this where you want our children to be at this hour?" She says, "Yes."

I don't know if it brings peace of mind knowing that her children are safe in their homes, but after this, she closes her eyes and quickly falls asleep.

Praxis

Carol's ability to conceptualize, plan, and interact with items in everyday life has degenerated considerably since she was diagnosed. She can still sign her name, but it is delicate and shaky. She's started to draw a circle around her signature, which she never did before. Her ability to jump from one thought to another is compromised, which seems like confusion due to FTD.

The recent example was in Dr. Devi's office when Carol was asked to write her name. She did fine. She was asked to write her granddaughter's name, and she did. She was asked to write my name, and there was a long pause. She wrote her granddaughter's name again.

This growing inability to jump from one thought to another is obvious in other aspects of her life. When Lika or I get her situated on the couch to watch TV, we ask her to lift her legs so she can rest them on an ottoman. She used to respond immediately. Now, I can see she thinks harder about completing the task or following other physical tasks with multistep instructions. Dr. Devi explained it as *praxis*, which involves a person generating an idea of *what* they want to do, figuring out *how* they will go about doing it, and then *doing* or carrying out what they want to do.

I can say that practicing meditation doesn't make everything right, and it doesn't make the experience of living with Carol's FTD good or help me feel okay about watching her live through such a ravaging disease. It is helping me find inner peace while being surrounded by war. I can see life with more clarity and be present with it. I don't like it, but there's nothing to say I must like it. It sounds peculiar, but I have more joy in my life because of this.

Finding Joy in Zimbabwe

Joy has a special interest for me. The first time I witnessed it was years ago on the banks of the Zambezi River in Zimbabwe. I didn't experience it personally, but I saw it with the people who lived in the country. I went there to write a story.

Zimbabwe is a landlocked country in the southern portion of Africa. The settlements of the Shona tribe traditionally consist of elder men and their extended families. My first impression was that they had little but the clothes on their backs. My first exposure to joy was sitting on the bank of the Zambezi River, and voices filled with song and regular eruptions of laughter came from across the river. I learned it was a small fishing community. They weren't celebrating any event but rather preparing to seine the river for fish. It struck me that in all my years living in America, I had not once heard such exuberance fill the streets where I lived, let alone imagine it as preparation for going to work.

Another example was when the guide I was with had the chance to spread the word about the availability of a downed Cape buffalo. This was a seventeen-hundred-pound animal. A human telegraph quickly developed as runners spread the word from hut to hut. We drove seven men and three women, one carrying her one-year-old child on her back, as close as we physically could to the carcass, and a half-mile hike through the bush remained. We were dropping them off at the site, and they would have to lug the food in burlap bags two miles back to their huts and repeat the chore multiple times on foot. Their light-hearted laughter, warm demeanors, looks of satisfaction, and inner contentment shone with brilliance on their faces. Joy was in their bodies; they felt it, despite the difficult circumstances they endured, and I could see it. Joy is the realization that the things we desire are the things we already possess.

Practicing meditation has helped me find joy. Joy is the peace found in being in the moment of what is happening to us. Life is my companion; I practice not editorializing about what it presents to me and not viewing it with prejudice. This was what the Shona felt when having to toil with the Cape buffalo. They understood it was the life they had, and they were simply living it and grateful for the food. They understood that life could be no different. Life may be easy or hard, but understanding that we can be with whatever we are faced with is transformative, and transformation is joy.

There is a link between joy and wonder. When we are open to a situation, we can learn from it and cope with it. I see wonder in the eyes of my grandchildren, as everything they look at is new and exciting. They explore out of curiosity; they don't know or care about why things are the way they are. They just marvel at them. They are in awe of colors, shapes, sizes, sounds, and how things feel. They have no judgments or questions, just amazement for sunrises, sunsets, slamming a door closed, throwing food, letting out a bloodcurdling scream, and everything else that is new to them.

Childlike Wonder

As an adult, I look at things and figure how they work, how I can use them, how they affect me, and how much they cost, and I make judgments about them to feel a sense of control. I want to know the influence they will have on my life. To my grandchildren, the same things are seen through eyes of wonder, excitement, and without preconceived ideas and prejudice.

Our need to understand things, have a sense of control over them, and our experience with them blinds us to the wonder and curiosity we had as children. We approach them with a set of assumptions, concepts, values, and practices that impose a reality that hides the magic of life.

We see in children that curiosity is the natural state of humans. It's what we are when we come into the world, and practicing meditation is our way back to it. The only difference is that our adult experiences provide us with wisdom that we don't have as children. It may take years, but practicing meditation breaks down the walls of our paradigms, and we experience wonder like children again. Life becomes the motivation to understand ourselves, and practice cultivates the ability to have the curiosity we did as children. We find the way to trust life to arrive as it is meant to and not respond with fear and preconceptions.

We are surrounded by tragic stories. Carol's FTD is a daily reminder of the pain others are experiencing. Experiencing life is the only way to understand the life of another. Raising our awareness and tapping into a higher consciousness through practice allows us to see beyond these situations with the wonder of children and understand what life is revealing to us.

It's also interesting to find that solutions come for the problems I'm confronted by: resources, knowledge, and people appear just when they are needed.

Carol and Bruce Willis

I don't watch the news on TV. I can think of a dozen reasons to own a TV but perhaps none better than to keep it turned off. I also haven't had a newspaper delivered to our home in nearly ten years. Although I sort through some headlines on the internet to keep involved in understanding world events, I find that the top stories and headlines center on death, disaster, and scandal. None of these have any positive effect on my life and certainly none that I have any influence over. I'm always amazed by the media's ability to take nothing and perfect it, but I don't need drama for drama's sake.

One day in February, I headed downstairs after work. The TV program Carol was watching ended, and the news came on. I caught the announcement that the actor Bruce Willis had been diagnosed with FTD. The family said that it was painful, but they were relieved to have a clear diagnosis. The news was a difficult blow. I hadn't known anyone else with FTD, and now there was someone famous with it.

There was an added reason that the news hit me so hard. I was friendly with Mr. Willis back in 1977 when we were both at Montclair State College, now known as Montclair State University. To this day I have never met someone with as much confidence, wit, charm, and boldness. At a time when young men wore their hair shoulder length or longer, did not wear earrings, and carried their books to class "in hand," this guy had his hair cropped to the scalp, wore an earring in one ear, and toted his books in what is today the ubiquitous backpack. Bruce was audacious but extremely likeable and ahead of his time.

When we went on our 1:00 a.m. trips to White Castle, which was more often than I care to admit, both patrons and workers couldn't ignore our arrival. Bruce was outgoing and boisterous and used these traits to deliver an impish but benign humor. His charm won over anyone initially offended, the proof being that they eventually joined in the laughter.

Anthony P. Mauro Sr.

I graduated and didn't see Bruce again until eight years later. I was watching the TV show *Moonlighting*, which revolved around the cases of a detective agency called Blue Moon. There were two partners, Madolyn "Maddie" Hayes (played by Cybill Shepherd) and David Addison Jr. (played by Bruce Willis). Yep, there he was with all his wise-cracking charm oozing from the TV. The rest is history.

I don't imagine Bruce would remember me now that forty-six years have passed. The purpose of my namedropping is that the announcement on the news drove home the point that FTD is a disease that afflicts our lives in different ways. He has the disease, and I am the guardian of a woman who has the disease. I am thankful that Bruce's celebrity will bring attention to the disease and do the same for a cure.

Compassion

As the years progress, Carol's cheery demeanor flourishes in the voids left by FTD. Even as pieces of her personality slowly vanish, they are replaced with love, made obvious by outbursts of happy handclapping, giggling, laughing, and singing. They are uplifting for me, my kids, and even the strangers in public who are usually startled by them at first.

Lively handclapping is now a constant companion. Friends ask me how it doesn't drive me crazy, but it's a matter of perspective. Each noisy eruption is proof that despite FTD, Carol is happy, and when she's clapping, I hear her happiness. I admit that there are occasions when I'm reading or watching TV after a long day and wish for quiet, but these are few and are quickly put back into perspective.

An interesting thing occurs as compassion grows from practicing meditation. I have found that caregiving isn't a burden as some might think but instead a positive experience. It's a masterful design for the advancement of humanity. We are not made whole by selfish service to our own needs but by selfless service to the needs of others. There is the sense of love when we provide care to another human being whose quality of life depends on us. I get satisfaction knowing that Carol is getting excellent care, and this model of care is expanding my children's view of life.

Productively coping with stressful circumstances is a transformative experience, and the sense of satisfaction is transferable to other areas of life. Practicing meditation is about giving, and I continue to gain an understanding of giving to others. I make mistakes, but that's fine, because they teach me that it's okay to say no at times or that becoming involved can sometimes be counterproductive. It takes experience to figure out what my life is.

Things like FTD don't happen to most of us, but minor things do. The images we have of how our lives should be or how we want them to be usually end up crumpled into a ball and tossed on the floor by the realities of life.

I can face life through practicing meditation and learn something, raise my awareness, wither the roots of my anxiety, and transform myself, or I can cause myself to suffer, and my suffering will transfer in real or nuanced ways to others. It isn't easy, but it is my choice. In striving to replicate the experience I had on the helicopter ride high above the Grand Canyon, I've discovered how to let go of the need to control.

If I want peace, joy, love, compassion, and wisdom, I will continue practicing meditation and experience life caring for Carol by caring for me.

Enjoy the ride. The ride is life.

Anthony P. Mauro Sr.

Appendix

Calming Method for Panic Attacks

I begin to breathe deeply with purpose and place awareness on each inhale and exhale. I acknowledge the irrational script I'm writing in my mind.

I redirect myself to be in the moment by focusing on the surroundings. I assign a severity number to my anxiety on a scale from one to ten, which helps me realize I can endure more anxiety, which in turn lessens my anxiety level.

The Six Realities That Cause Us Suffering Due to Attachments

1. We all die

2. We all experience illness

3. We all age

4. We all lose things we love

5. We all lose people we love

6. Every second of life is change

Practicing Meditation

- I become aware of my breathing.

- I slowly attune to the sensation of air moving in and out of my body.

- I feel my diaphragm rise and fall as the air enters and leaves my nostrils.

- I witness my thoughts without judgment.

- I acknowledge my thoughts without judgment.

- I witness and feel my emotions.

- I witness and feel my body sensations.

Anthony P. Mauro Sr.

Photos

Carol and me at Tori's wedding

Carol at sixty-three years old

Carol at thirty years old

Anthony P. Mauro Sr.

Carol and Tori on Tori's wedding day

Me, Andrew, Tori, Carol, Anthony Jr., and Gina

Lynn, Carol, Lee, and Carol's mother, Marion

Carol and me preparing for our hot air balloon ride

Anthony P. Mauro Sr.

Carol in the pumpkin house

*Carol in her favorite Jeep. We use this
for our nightly rides together*

Carol and Anthony Jr. (mother and son
wedding dance)

Anthony P. Mauro Sr.

Carol with our granddaughter, Charli

Carol, me, and our grandson, AJ

Caring for Carol by Caring for Me   229

Carol, me, and the helicopter that began my
journey into meditation and self-discovery

Anthony P. Mauro Sr.

Printed in Great Britain
by Amazon